MYSTIC
MOOSETALES

MYSTIC MOOSETALES

REDEFINING WILDLIFE

ROBIN MCMILLAN

A SUPERNATURAL ALLEGORY

DEDICATION

I dedicate this book to Donna, my wife of 36 years, and
to my four children and their families. How they have
enriched my life!

ACKNOWLEDGEMENTS

I would be remiss not to acknowledge four unique friends: Rick, Steve, Leo, and Bob. You have enriched me, at times enraged me, always envisioned me -boredom was never an option. I would be a lesser man without your influence. May God's richest blessing be yours.

ENDORSEMENTS

Stories tell us many things. For most of us, other people's stories are the easiest way to learn life's lessons. *Moose Tales* takes storytelling to a whole new level, illustrating life in both the natural and the supernatural. This is a great read that will make you think, cry, laugh and apply. It is creativity at its best.

Beni Johnson, Bethel Church, Redding CA
Author, *The Happy Intercessor*

Robin McMillan has been a personal friend for nearly twenty years. We have different backgrounds, but have similarities in interesting areas: We are both pastors and have a genuine love for God's people. We are passionate about Christ and the outpouring of His Holy Spirit. We also love the supernatural presence of the Lord, and appreciate God's sense of humor, joy, and laughter. Robin's new book uses all three of these to take us on an amazing adventure. *Mystic Moose Tales* will delight your heart and inspire your soul to experience the tangible glory of God in the now! Every page makes you hungry for more. Get ready for fresh joy in God's presence as you enter the *Mystic Moose Tales*.

Mahesh Chavda,
Senior Pastor, All Nations Church
Charlotte, NC

It has been said that "reality is stranger than fiction". I believe this to be true and I also believe that good fiction helps us see reality in a new light. Jesus Himself never spoke without a story. Certainly not all His parables were fiction, but each was an illustration: a truth with implications that reached far beyond the story itself and helped us to see our world differently. Mystic Moose exists somewhere between *Tom Sawyer* and the *Chronicles of Narnia,* but what makes *Moose Tales* fascinating is that the most ridiculous parts of this story could be true.

John Mark McMillan
Singer Song Writer
Charlotte, NC

In the allegorical tradition of John Bunyan and C. S. Lewis comes *Mystic Moose Tales* by Robin McMillan. Drawing on his own extensive walk with the Lord, McMillan has created a talking moose with a lot more to share than Balaam's donkey. Readers who spend time with Mystic Moose will be entertained, challenged, encouraged, and inspired.

Robert Whitlow
Best-selling author of *Water's Edge*
Charlotte, NC

INTRODUCTION
TO MYSTIC MOOSETALES:
REDEFINING WILDLIFE

My primary purpose for writing this book is to impart two things to the current generation: love for Jesus and authentic hunger for the historic supernatural God of the Bible. I chose the allegorical style because it lends itself to creativity in a wide range of expression and humor. C.S. Lewis, J.R.R. Tolkein, John Bunyan, Joel Chandler Harris, and others used allegory to impart life changing concepts and realities. I like that.

I wrote it from a 'Southern' perspective, for that is what I am, a child of the South. I have not focused on being unique or original, just honest. Honest expression has the potential to touch people in authentic life changing ways. C.S. Lewis wrote: "Even in literature and art, no man who bothers about originality will ever be original: whereas if you simply try to tell the truth (without caring two pence how often it has been told before) you will, nine times out of ten, become original without ever having noticed it."

I sought to present these stories in a humorous fashion. Who can flourish without joy and humor? Not me. Nehemiah said that *'the joy of the Lord is your strength.'* Joy and humor dilute the stress of life and give us the strength and resilience, not only to endure but to overcome. The Lord's own joy personally imparted to us is our strength.

The gift of imagination fueled the expansion of successful human endeavor in every era. It is a wonderful tool when used in a redemptive visionary way. Paul the apostle prayed for the Ephesian church, that God might energize their sanctified imaginations: *'that the eyes of your heart may be enlightened'.* Jesus said *'all things are possible to him that believes'.* For us to experience *those* things we must exercise an imaginative faith. Here I have attempted to exercise my own imagination to inspire my readers to live lives of just such possibility and adventure.

God urged Elijah the prophet to use his imagination in a time of crisis. The Lord said to him:

> **"'Arise, go to Zarephath, which belongs to Sidon, and dwell there. *See*, I have commanded a widow there to provide for you.' So he arose and went to Zarephath. And when he came to the gate of the city, indeed a widow was there gathering sticks"** (I Kings 17:8-10).

The Lord told Elijah to *see* something that he could not see with his physical eyes. He not only had to find the widow, but to convince her to trust God with him for their survival. By faith the prophet went to Zarephath, found the very woman, and convinced her to do what God wanted her to do. What a marvelous story.

As a child I sat at the feet of my great Aunt Louise as she read to me J. Calvin Reid's book *Bird Life in Wington*. The book consisted of morality parables taken from the life of a community of birds as they spoke to one another and interacted in human ways. Joel Chandler Harris' *Uncle Remus Stories* are another example of that kind of literature. Uncle Remus was a fictional black man that Harris used as a vehicle to tell stories depicting the foibles of human nature through the imagery of animals. Those tales revealed the importance of wisdom as a necessary tool for life. As Brother Bear and Brother Fox sought to eat Brother Rabbit, and as he sought to outwit both of them, the great themes of human nature such as life and death, greed and trickery, arrogance and humility, were identified and explored. And then there is *Aesop's Fables*, ancient tales involving animals and the lessons one may glean from them.

In my imagination there exists a world where animals walk on two legs, demonstrate all the attributes of humans, and live and interact together with people. In just such a world Theodore Conquest 'Mystic' Moose lives and does his exploits. Many of these tales are based on events that have literally happened to flesh and blood men and women. These people I know. Other events originate from lives of historic Christians I don't know but have read about or heard their testimonies. Some of his adventures are uniquely his own, yet the essence of them, or one could say the spirit of them, are ones any of us can have if we qualify.

"How does one qualify for such adventures?"

I am glad you asked that question. One qualifies by meeting Jesus Christ, by being born another time from heaven by the agency of the Spirit of God, and by being filled with the Holy Spirit. This experience is uniquely Christian. Some of you reading this book may have rejected the Christian life. I can understand if you have. So much of what has driven down the religious highway is offensive. It is easy to understand why many would reject Him because of the kind of life demonstrated by some of His followers. They may not be wonderful, but Jesus certainly is.

Satan, our very real enemy, has been behind the alienation of many people from the Lord. We must see through all the reasons he has provided to keep us from the purposes of God in this generation. There is much to do, and there are few who have enough vision and courage to do it. Now is the time for you to *see*. Just like Elijah, use the eyes of your imagination and you will see that nothing is impossible to the man, the woman, the boy or girl who walks with God. God Himself is offering you a personal invitation to do so.

So, come enter the world of Theodore Moose and discover anew this realm of God and the possibilities He has for you in this life. The world is waiting for you, needs you, is even crying out for you! Come, for this is your day.

TABLE OF

CONTENTS

CHAPTER 1

MYSTERIOUS MOOSE MEETING

There are times in life when specific events alter your very destiny. You know it when it happens. Other times you discover *it* later. My encounter with Mystic Moose fell into category number two.

He scared me early on, the first talking moose I ever met. He walked on two legs and acted much more human than many who were human. I had heard about this category of being and of the mystical Moose that had supposedly done great things. Only later, as events unfolded, did I realize how much meeting him changed my life. For that I shall be ever thankful.

In the twilight of his amazing life, the ninety-year old Moose slept peacefully before me. Having dozed while reading his Bible, his half-frame reading glasses eased down his large grizzled nose. His massive antlers, scarred from the years, exuded an ancient quality. Molting season made patches of shedding antler hang from them like a moss draped Savannah, Georgia oak. His burnished brown hair, peppered with silver gray, spoke of his maturity. The years creased his muzzle-like face in a hundred different places, like country roads on a well-worn map. With one hand he barely held on to a well-worn copy of an ancient book as it lay beside him on the bed. He had underlined, noted, and highlighted one particular sentence as though he had read it ten thousand times.

> **"But He was wounded for our transgressions, He was bruised for our iniquities; the chastisement of our peace was upon Him, and by His stripes we are healed."** [1]

This description of my first encounter with Mystic Moose occurred in the well-appointed home of Magellan Matthews. Magellan, an independently wealthy gentleman, explored the globe as casually as a shopper walks through the store aisles of his neighborhood mall. On impulse that day, I stopped by his house to discuss an interview Magellan agreed to give me. *World Archeological Magazine* assigned me to write an article featuring his recent expedition to South America where he viewed firsthand the effects of the diminishing rain forests upon the ecology and wildlife of the region. As an internationally acclaimed archaeologist and ecologist, his views carried much weight in the scientific community.

Legend has it that Magellan met Mystic Moose under extraordinary circumstances in the Congo's deep jungle many years earlier. Over the years they became close friends, so the Moose stayed in Magellan's guesthouse when the opportunity presented itself. Their hectic schedules and diverse travels made such visits rare but rewarding. As

---

1   Isaiah 53:5

I later learned, the Moose appeared unexpectedly on Magellan's doorstep the day before I came by. At his age the traveling and ministry schedule Mystic Moose maintained wearied him. His longing for the comraderie of his oldest and closest colleague drew him back to Magellan's home once again.

The guest room where he rested was paneled in dark walnut with a lush fern green rug covering the center of the knotty pinewood floors. The richness of the surroundings impressed me almost as much as this Moose who lay snoring quietly before me. As we entered the room together, Magellan pulled open one of the blinds to let in the morning sun. I assumed he still slept, as a shaft of light piercing the room's darkness illuminated him before me.

SUDDENLY HE SPOKE!

"He told me you were coming," his rumbling voice sounded like gravel pouring out of the bed of a big dump truck as it broke the room's silence.

"Excuse me?" I stammered, startled both by the timbre of his voice and his sudden, unusual remark.

His unexpected comment baffled me. As I mentioned, my visit to Magellan's house wasn't planned. Interestingly enough, for years I pursued interviewing Mystic Moose but could never track him down. His elusive lifestyle and erratic travel to far-flung places made meeting him extremely difficult. The legends surrounding his supernatural abilities and encounters with God provoked many to seek him for help. Some sought him for his remarkable wisdom; others needed healing for themselves or someone they loved. Those he trusted did not easily reveal his whereabouts, especially since he had grown older. If Magellan had not told me that he was in the guest room and invited me to meet him, I would not have known he was there.

My Strange Conversation Continues

"Yes, He told me you were coming today," Mystic Moose continued.

"Who told you I was coming?"

I heard so much about this iconoclastic moose, much of which, quite frankly, troubled me. I am a freelance writer and photo-journalist, a life I chose because of my inquisitive nature. Tales of the miraculous events surrounding this Moose were so beyond the norm that I decided to investigate him myself. If Mystic Moose proved to be a sham as others I had exposed, then I would gladly uncover him also. If I wrote a best-selling book from my research, that would be good, too. I did need to make a living.

Background on Angus McAlpine

In my travels I saw much that caused me to question God's existence or, at the very least, His interest in any of us. My photo documentaries of the ethnic cleansing in Eastern Europe and other armed conflicts I covered for NBS news exposed me to humanity's worst. "What kind of God would allow such evil?" I questioned not so secretly. The recent death of my wife Marilyn didn't help. We were married for thirty years. Her sudden death staggered me beyond belief. She had a weak area in a blood vessel close to her heart that ruptured during an operation to repair it, and she died on the operating room table. My devastation fueled a quiet rage and the confusion that muddied my thoughts, amplifying the emptiness I felt. Life turned dark, and depression gained ground on me about the time I met Mystic Moose.

Little did I know that I would soon receive comfort for my heart's deep sorrow and resolution to my life long searchings. The avenue for those answers sat in front of me this very morning as I stood before this elderly mysterious moose, genus -**Alces Americana Southeranas**.

MYSTIC MOOSE CONTINUED

"An angel told me all about you, the one I first met as a small boy struggling to earn my 'Courage and Bravery' badge in the Animal Scouts, deep in the South Carolina woods. Last night that same angel told me to expect you around 10:00 this morning," he spoke in that even, gravelly, matter-of-fact voice that I came to appreciate.

From out in the hall the great grandfather clock sounded, one bell following another until ten rang out. With it still echoing in my ears, I thought to myself, "Ten o'clock indeed!"

Mystic continued, "At times the Lord shows me things that are going to happen in the future. I am rarely surprised any more. If Jesus doesn't tell me, then often one of His angels will. Sometimes the Holy Spirit shows me events in a dream the night before, other times in a vision. I have seen things many years ahead, even in the middle of strangely unrelated circumstances," his voice trailed off.

Mystic Moose's responses stunned me. Magellan had yet to introduce us. No one, including Magellan, knew I was coming over -no one.

Magellan began our introduction, "Mystic, may I introduce to you…"

"I know who this is, Magellan," Mystic interrupted. "I know exactly who R. Angus McAlpine is. I have waited to meet him for many years. I saw this very event in a vision years ago under extremely unusual circumstances. Why, it happened as I lay shackled in chains in the dusty prison hut of the aboriginal Kamtuti tribe in a dark region of the African subcontinent. While preaching there I enraged the local witch doctor who accused me of being responsible for the sudden death of his king. My, I was in a tight spot!"

I could tell that Mystic's mind wandered a moment, but he refocused and got back on track.

"Please indulge this old man's memories, but in that vision I saw (as he pointed a long finger my way) *this* man… and I heard the Lord speak his name to me out loud: *R. Angus McAlpine.*

"Jesus showed me years ago that He picked *you* to tell my story. I know you've been looking for me, that you want to write my story or some story about a realm you have little knowledge of or belief in. Your timing and your focus for the book have been wrong. What you want to write and what He wants you to write are two different things. Why, you would have written a book infused with your doubt. This generation is floating in a sea of hopelessness. They need something, or rather Someone to believe in!

"Half the number of all people who ever lived on earth are alive today, and half of them are under twenty years old. They need an authentic encounter with the supernatural God of the Bible…One who is presented to them in creative life-changing ways. Then they will speak of Him unashamedly and demonstrate His power to a world that desperately needs to see Him as He really is. Now is the time."

"Wh-what are you talking about?" I stammered.

Mystic continued, "I am convinced that God will do something extraordinary in these days with many people, not just a few. The Prophet Daniel referred to this epoch in his book:

"… the people who know their God shall be strong, and carry out great exploits." [2]

"Listen to me, R. Angus McAlpine. You have been chosen to write a book that will challenge and encourage a generation for a time like this one! Few believe God will send an earth shaking awakening that will alter the course of the world again. But it shall happen. Why, it has already begun!"

---

2   Daniel 11:32

6

McAlpine is Baffled by the Conversation

Mystic Moose's remarks dumbfounded me. We never met before. Now he not only called me by name, but he knew my desire to write about him. Only my wife Marilyn knew of the incomplete manuscript that I worked on for years, a book on famous contemporary Christians. Part of it put a microscope on those who claimed to operate in the 'so-called' supernatural power of God. I intended to discredit any charlatans and give an accurate understanding of the absence of God's personal activity in the world. It currently sat in a dusty box beneath my bed. No book of its nature would be complete without an interview or chapter about this Mystic Moose whose abrupt comments left me staggering.

I stood speechless by his bed, listening to him with my jaw hanging open. Some who knew of Mystic Moose's reputation explained that he often knew things he had no natural way of knowing. I never believed them, but now his words and this entire experience absolutely mystified me. I could not refute the fact that he knew things about me that no one else knew.

Magellan's First Meeting With Mystic Moose

Magellan Matthews told me that he met Mystic Moose under incredible, even spurious, circumstances. Mystic referred to it earlier when he mentioned the so-called vision he had of me while shackled in the prison hut of the Kamtuti tribe who happened to be cannibalistic at the time. Mystic's gospel preaching enraged them the first time he visited their village. So, they decided to eat him as the main course at one of their new moon feasts.

At the same time, but in another part of the sub-continent on an archeological expedition, Magellan Matthews was among a more civilized tribe who stopped eating their enemies more than a decade earlier. He was searching for the ancient ruins of Zinj, a fabled lost African city rumored to contain the gold mines of King Solomon, when unbelievable tales surfaced, tales of a Moose with supernatural powers he used among the area tribes to evangelize them.

One rumor told of a tribal king raised from the dead by the power of this Moose's prayer. It happened while Mystic Moose visited a notoriously hostile tribe to preach the gospel. However, as the gospel-preaching Moose entered town and approached the lodge of the king, the old boy dropped dead from a heart attack. The tribe, led by the community witch doctor, accused Mystic Moose of being the bad medicine that ended the king's life. They decided to eat the Moose.

Mystic Moose later gave me this blow-by-blow account of his African adventure:

"As I was lying shackled in that nasty prison hut, I heard the approaching hubbub of the funeral procession of the dead pygmy chief draw near.

"I muttered to myself, 'How did I ever get into this mess?' Then I remembered. Bertha Belch! She was responsible for getting me to Africa. The powerful testimony of the famous lady missionary, with her tales of God's miraculous moving among the natives, lured me to the African mission field. One fall our church invited missionaries for a week of special services emphasizing world evangelism. Pastor J.T. Stumper arose with unbridled enthusiasm and announced:

> *Ladies and gentlemen, it is our distinct privilege to have as our guest speaker one of the foremost female pioneer missionary evangelists to the continent of darkest Africa. For years we have been anticipating her visit. The testimony of her remarkable success in ministry among some of the unreached tribes will present foreign missions as a most adventurous career for those of you called to just such a life of faith. She will be our special missionary speaker at next Sunday's morning service. Come hear Bertha Belch, all the way from darkest Africa.*

"As a little boy moose I thought, 'Good Lord, you mean you can hear this lady belch all the way from Africa?' Obviously, I was not paying close attention to the announcements. All I heard was that some woman named Bertha was going to burp in church the next Lord's Day morning and you could hear her all the way from the Dark Continent. Anyone who could be heard belching all the way from Africa was someone I wanted to meet. It was only during the service that I realized that she was not actually going to belch but that the pastor had made a semantic 'faux pas' by the way he made his announcement. Still, I went to the meeting and was most impressed with Miss Belch, *all the way from Africa*. I decided that Sunday morning to visit her part of the world when I grew up.

"Now I was *in* Africa, languishing in that hell hole as first choice on the demented witch doctor's menu, being prepared to be eaten and wind up *in* the bellies of some very hostile hostiles! As the funeral procession approached, the strange singing and frenetic dancing of the natives snapped me back to reality in an instant.

"I stood up and looked through the slats of the prison house at the oncoming entourage. I prayed aloud, 'Jesus, I'm in a tight spot. You've gotta help me.'"

A Sudden Vision

Suddenly the Lord appeared to Mystic in a vivid vision, one of the clearest ones he had ever seen.

Jesus said, "Shout out as loud as you can. Tell the dead King to get up. Tell him three times to do so, in My name."

The vision ended as suddenly as it began. Mystic began to sweat bullets, realizing that he was about to be the main course at dinner that night. Mystic could see a fire crackling under a big black cook pot the witch doctor set up outside his quarters. The rising smoke shrouded the scene in pagan mystery. Gunju, the deranged old witch doctor danced wildly as he grinned hungrily in the direction of the incarcerated Moose, every once in a while stirring the cook pot with his shrunken skeleton headed staff.

"Fresh meat! Fresh meat!" he said as he drooled and moaned over and over, relishing the upcoming meal of moose meat. He began dancing frenetically around the cauldron, stirring up a dry and suffocating cloud of dust with his weathered old feet.

As the funeral procession passed by, Mystic suddenly shouted out at the top of his lungs, "Stop the procession, I have a message from my God."

His words rang with such authority and clarity that the very sound of his voice stopped everyone dead in their tracks, silencing the myriad of moaning mourners.

MYSTIC COMMANDS

Then Mystic Moose barked out the authoritative command, "King Ayotundi Babajeed, rise from your funeral pallet in the name of Jesus Christ." Mystic hesitated a moment and then spoke twice more, "Rise from your funeral pallet in the name of Jesus Christ. Rise from your funeral pallet in the name of Jesus Christ."

Gunju began to laugh out loud at such a foolish notion. "No one rises from the dead," he squealed in mocked delight. His hideous laughter was clearly demonic. "And you will be my dinner as soon as the old boy is buried." The voice with which he spoke sounded like the deep guttural growl of some wild jungle animal.

AN AMAZING OCCURRENCE

Then a most amazing thing happened. The silver and blue cockatoo feathers on King Babajeed's burial headdress began to quiver, faintly at first, then again. Some later said they thought the wind was blowing them. Then they shook again for the third time, this time more violently, though the air was as deathly still as was the old dead African king. When they shook that time, some in the burial procession began to murmur nervously. Suddenly, the king sneezed loudly and sat upright. Grown women swooned and began blubbering incoherently, some falling headlong in the dust while grizzled and grey bearded men gasped with saucer sized eyes at the resurrected king. Most of the children panicked and stampeded in hysterical fear.

King Babajeed opened his eyes and focused on his surroundings. He shook his head several times, then lovingly looked for a long moment at his wife, Queen Uzoma. He gazed at the funeral party consisting of his children, his grandchildren, and many of his lifelong friends and loyal subjects. With great effort he tried to maintain his composure but began weeping silently. Dusty from the funeral procession, the king's tears ran down his face forming small rivulets. As the tears flowed, they forged tiny, clear trails as they washed away the dust from his bearded cheeks, slowly flowing down to drip upon his brilliant white and royal blue burial robes.

Despair to Joy

No one said anything; they were all too afraid. The deafening silence seemed to last a lifetime. Then Queen Uzoma began shouting for joy. She had been mourning the loss of the love of her life with heartbreaking agony. Over and again she shouted her husband's name, "Ayotundi Babajeed. Ayotundi Babajeed." Suddenly, the rest of the tribe began to shout with her "Ayotundi Babajeed. Ayotundi Babajeed." For his first name meant "joy has returned" and his second name meant "father has come to life again." The joy of her life had returned, even from the dead! Others began to shout and dance as the funeral procession instantly became a huge celebration.

Finally, King Babajeed sat up on the funeral pallet, motioning with his right hand and quieting the people. The feathers in his kingly crown started moving slightly in the cool breeze that now began to blow.

His Unbelievable Tale

"I have had the most dreadful experience," he said. "I have been to a place that I never believed existed, even in my darkest nightmares. It is a place of unimaginable dread. When I died, the most hideous being suddenly appeared and took control of me. As he clutched my elbow with his cold vice-like grip, I knew I was in deep trouble. His touch alone flooded my soul with unspeakable horror. I could not escape his grasp nor bring myself to look at his hideous countenance but caught his leering glare from the corner of my eye.

"Remember, people, as your king I have proven my courage many times. I have stared down the midnight black panther, fought the lion tooth and claw, and danced the dance of death without flinching, face to face with the great fanged, blue-jowled baboon with protruding hind quarters. I have never retreated in the day of battle and never known fear a day in my life... until this day! You must heed my words. Do whatever you must to avoid that horrible chasm."

A Most Terrible Pit

The king continued, "Down, down, down he and I decended, into the most terrible pit imaginable. Oppressive heat, unquenchable thirst, and morbid hopelessness fueled the fiery atmosphere of that place. Instead of air, its inhabitants breathe a mixture of sour throat raking fumes filled with fear, pregnant with unbearable panic and racking anxiety. Unanswered cries of despair and loneliness and horrible howls of anguish echoed through the caverns of that infernal region. I could only imagine the terrified beings that birthed such piercing wails. As I descended, the tug of this irresistible and hideously evil force pulled me deeper and deeper into that pit of despair. Words alone will never convey the horror."

The king hesitated a moment. Now the tears were streaming down his face in sheets. "But when all hope seemed lost, I heard a voice, faint at first then gradually louder, cascading down to me from above, as though from another world.

"'King Ayotundi Babajeed, rise from your funeral pallet in the name of Jesus Christ!' When I heard that cry, faint as it was, the evil being who clutched my elbow in his deathly grip turned in panic. I watched as his evil confidence immediately drained from his wretched face. He began staring up toward the direction of the voice he heard. Then I heard it again, 'King Ayotundi Babajeed, rise from your funeral pallet in the name of Jesus Christ!' The evil being loosed his vice-like grip of my arm and fled in confused panic shouting, 'Oh no! Do not speak that name to me. Do not speak His name to me again. I cannot stand to hear that name!'

"Then I started rising up, farther and farther away from the oppressive region where I was taken. Then once more and much louder I heard, 'King Ayotundi Babajeed, rise from your funeral pallet in the name of Jesus Christ!'"

By now the king sobbed as his body shook with emotion. Speaking before the throng of tribal members, he continued, "The third time I heard that voice, I opened my eyes lying here on this funeral pallet, alive once more!"

With a new joy sparkling in his eyes, the king leapt down from his deathbed and demanded, "Bring me the one who commanded me to rise from the dead! His words contain life!"

OUT OF JAIL

Mystic continued, "At that, the king's guards rushed in the door of my miserable quarters and unchained me. They hastily carried me up to the small rise where King Babajeed now stood with Queen Uzoma. I explained how Jesus, another King, suffered for his sins, how His death paid for the king's eternal ransom from that place he just visited, and that he should put his trust in this King Jesus who rose from the dead for him. He fell on his face in the dust, regarding neither his regal burial clothes nor the opinions of his watching subjects, and grabbed me around the feet in unbridled appreciation. I will never forget his simple declaration of faith.

"He stood erect, turned toward all who watched, and boldly proclaimed before them all, 'I submit myself to this King you call Jesus!'

"Then many of his followers followed us to the nearby river where I was going to baptize the king in water. I also told them the good news that God's mercy in sending His Son to die for the sins of the world would save all who believed from going to the horrible place the king described to them. His entire tribe quietly and reverently listened to me before I baptized King Babajeed. Before the Queen was baptized, she said, 'My mother gave me this name, Uzoma. It means *to follow the right road.* Today I finally live up to that name. I urge all of you to follow me as well!!' Hundreds followed them into the river to do the same, demonstrating their newfound faith in Christ Jesus. Many of them began to speak in new languages empowered by the Holy Spirit as they emerged from the river where they were immersed."

MANY BURN EVIL ITEMS

"Many of the natives burned their articles of witchcraft and instruments of enchantment. Even the old witch doctor turned from his evil ways and quit practicing black magic. As Jesus set him free, he experienced an authentic gut-wrenching deliverance from the evil spirit that empowered him for the many years he was a witch doctor. He became an effective evangelist to the neighboring tribes."

THE LIGHT SPREADS

"The message about Jesus Christ spread from tribe to tribe in that once dark part of the continent. Amazing miracles occurred as I preached from village to village. I hesitate to describe them to you for fear that you will think I am absolutely crazy, but they are true. One of the most amazing ones occurred during the series of events that began with the witch doctor's deliverance. A young pygmy gave his life to the Lord asking me to lay hands on him and pray for him. I asked him what he wanted. He told me that, even for a pygmy, he was short. He wanted me to pray that he would, well, let me tell you in his own words: 'Give me the gift of height.'"

UNUSUAL MIRACLES

"I never heard that there was such a gift, but the young man's sincerity convinced me to pray for him as he requested.

"So I laid my hands on him and said, 'In the name of Jesus, be it to you even as you believe.'

"He began growing before my very eyes. I was so shocked that I began to laugh. Finally, after about four minutes, he stopped growing and was almost 6'6". He grew 32" before the miracle stopped. His clothes ripped as he grew and his sandals looked like they were shrinking because of the increase in his foot size. His people who stood there with him quickly wrapped a nearby blanket around him as his clothes gave way to his mysterious growth spurt. He had seen NBA basketball games on TV at a mission hospital near his village and wanted to play ever since, but he knew that he was too painfully small. His name was Bozzy Bolokii. Last I heard, he was playing guard with the Harlem Globetrotters."

MAGELLAN INVESTIGATES

Quickly, news of the amazing outpouring of the Holy Spirit among the Kamtuti tribe spread 100 miles north, reaching Magellan's camp. He temporarily interrupted his search for the city of Zinj to investigate. That was many years ago. Now the same fascinating Moose lay in bed in Magellan's guesthouse telling me, R. Angus McAlpine, that the Lord showed him I was to write his life's story.

Mystic Continues

"Yes," continued Mystic Moose, "it was while shackled in that prison hut, crying out to Jesus for deliverance, just before He gave me the key to raising King Babajeed from the dead, that I had an amazing vision of you. The Lord audibly spoke your name to me and showed me that one day you would write my life story! I never cease to be amazed at the odd times and interesting ways the Lord speaks. There I was, scared to death, on the verge of being slaughtered when the Lord showed me today's meeting with you clear as day.

"I was happy just to get off the menu! However, for King Ayotundi Babajeed to rise from the dead, for the entire village to give their lives to Jesus, for the witch doctor to be delivered and begin to evangelize, to see Bozzy Bolokii's miracle, have my life miraculously spared, *and* see my future with you, well, that is exceeding abundantly above all that I either asked or thought!"

Back to Sleep

Then Mystic Moose closed his eyes, turned away from me, pulled his covers up under his chin, and fell fast asleep. He was quietly snoring within a few moments. Magellan and I silently eased out of his room.

I shook my head in disbelief. "Who is this Mystic Moose?"

CHAPTER 2

THE MIRACULOUS BIRTH

The next morning I returned to Magellan's home hoping to begin interviewing Mystic Moose. I had not planned to return so soon but slept very little the previous night. The peculiar nature of our introduction affected me in an unusual way, being both intrigued and unsettled in ways I did not understand. I couldn't stay away.

Before going, I phoned Magellan's home several times, but after listening to his answering machine one time too many, I returned uninvited and once again, unexpected, or so I thought.

When I arrived, Magellan welcomed me warmly and escorted me through his home and out the back door. Mystic Moose sat across the large bricked patio in a rocking chair under a broad pecan tree. At first glance I noticed him with a plaid blanket covering his legs, warming himself in the sun and enjoying the crisp fall air that bright morning. His ever-present Bible was in his lap. He seemed to be in deep contemplation. I hesitated to disturb him, but Magellan encouraged me to go ahead. Mystic had been asking for me and told Magellan earlier to expect me that morning, to send me straight back when I arrived. He knew I was coming. Imagine that.

The brilliant early morning sun almost blinded me as I walked toward him out of the shadows of the house into the light. Mystic's supernatural stories from the previous day stirred long dormant memories of my youth. As I crossed the divide from the house to his chair, in a flash my mind reached back to my childhood religious experience. I saw myself sitting in the cold sterile church building my parents took me to as a child. Once again I smelled the musty odor and felt the uncomfortable sense of being there in the meeting, so formal and bland. I hated going. As a young child I imagined God must be the same way, cold, distant, and musty smelling like that old building they called *His* house. I shuddered at the memory. Who would want to know a God like that?

By my teenage years, church had long since been irrelevant. I classified my spiritual life as *personal,* meaning that discussions about it I didn't originate were off limits, to everybody, even to Marilyn. I had not been in church in years. I never considered going back once I set my sights on a career in journalism. My work and marriage to my childhood sweetheart *Miss Marilyn Johnson* were all I needed in this life, so I thought.

Under Observation

Though I was unaware, Mystic Moose watched me cross the garden from his rocker. Because of the angle of the sun, I couldn't tell that he was looking at me until I got closer. Over the last few steps, I felt his penetrating gaze.

"Bad church experiences can certainly affect one's concept of God, can they not, Angus?" Mystic said.

Mystic's compassionate expression betrayed an air of wisdom as once again he spoke to me as though our conversation began without me! I had no personal relationship with him, yet he knew things about me I had never told him, or anyone for that matter. At times he made me quite uncomfortable, but after I left him I usually felt quite encouraged.

How Did He Know These Things?

Later, Mystic taught me about spiritual gifts the Holy Spirit gives and how they operate in his life, enabling him to serve and help people just as he helped me when we first met. One gift is called a 'word of knowledge', and another, a 'word of wisdom'[3]. Each one contains insights, vital facts, internal perceptions, or particular pieces of wisdom for living and encouragement. Over the years God gave Mystic much understanding about the gifts, how they operate and how much they help people when used in love. He discovered that God often changed people's lives in powerful ways when Mystic told them vital facts or events they knew he had no logical or practical way to know. Sharing something that only they and God know releases faith and hope in their hearts in a way that almost no other experience can. God becomes very real to them as they realize how much He cares and wants to help them.

No one in my church ever talked about these things, so I was ignorant of these truths. Mystic showed me in the New Testament where Jesus used these same gifts to help people believe in Him and receive help[4]. He taught from Paul's first letter to the Corinthian church that God expects all believers to enthusiastically seek Him for

---

3   1 Corinthians 12:7-10

4   John 1:43-51, 4:7-26

these gifts[5]. They are a blessing from God to be used both as spiritual weapons of war in our everyday lives for protection, and tools to help build up others. When people live without using these gifts, it's like being an unarmed soldier sent into battle.

Mystic ached over the many believers in the church today who do not believe in the gifts and who assume anyone using them must be involved in something demonic or evil. The real gifts are not aspects of the new age or e.s.p. or some kind of occult practice, as some believe today, but are a result of dependence upon and the infilling of the Holy Spirit.

Over the years many well-meaning Christians who were confused and/or ignorant of how the gifts operated accused Mystic of being evil. He knew that many of the same Christians that did not believe in the gifts supported missionaries on foreign fields who regularly functioned in them in order to survive in such hostile demonic environments. In many cases the missionaries' lives and ministries depended upon the proper use of the gifts, yet many of them never spoke of using them in their home churches for fear of losing their support.

OUR CONVERSATION CONTINUED

"Mystic, I don't like anything about church," I said. "It never made sense to me. I quit going when I was in junior high school. The church I went to as a child was populated by senior citizens and their parents."

"I went through times of doubt myself," said Mystic. "At times my church experience was irrelevant and boring, but my family history included different periods of time when God supernaturally intervened in our lives. I call these episodes 'visitations from God'. These visitations helped encourage us and continued to show us the way into our destinies. We had some incredible experiences with Him. In

---

5   1 Corinthians 12:31, 14:31

fact, I'd never have been born except for God's miraculous activity in my mother's life during one of these 'visitations'."

Then Mystic Moose recounted one of the most remarkable tales I have ever heard. Much of it is hard to believe, but I have related it here just as he told it.

THE DAYS OF BARRENNESS ARE OVER

Mystic began, "That early March evening, a bitter, wet wind blew into town, that miserable kind of wet cold people expected that time of year in our small sleepy Southern town. I was told that during the winter I was born, the days seemed as short as a Siberian spring and as dark as mid-winter there, yet the sun shined warmly in the hearts of my parents, Herbert and Monica Moose. Mom's contractions began earlier in the day, food induced, as Moose contractions do. (They began just after she finished her tuna fish sandwich, a half mega-bag of barbecue potato chips, and a quart of butter pecan ice cream!) Every eighteen minutes waves of pain would rise, crest, and then recede. Mom did not resent these painful contractions. To her they were the bittersweet evidence of victories gained and promises fulfilled.

"Before I was born, my mom wanted a child more than anyone could imagine. She had all but lost hope of ever having one, until the ten-foot angel *first* appeared to our family and she received her miraculous healing. Now, as the contractions grew closer together and more intense, their anticipation of my birth mounted. My folks' extraordinary struggle to have a child was almost over, and the haunting years of barrenness would soon be but a memory."

THE HEALING HEAT

"As I mentioned, Mom was not physically able to bear children. 'Impotence' they called it! She went to two regular MDs and some specialists and took test after test only to be disappointed time and again. Mom couldn't conceive and so her heart broke. Then one hot July evening during a prayer meeting, her close friend Julia Skunk, knowing my mother's heartbrokenness, prayed down the power. Mom felt an unusual heat start to build up in her lower abdomen as Julia prayed, laying her hands on her back. 'Oh Lord Jesus,' Julia prayed at the top of her lungs, 'let Your power fall on Monica now! Restore her body and let her bear a child in view of Your great goodness. In Jesus' name!'

"Julia didn't pray that once. She asked insistently over and again. She prayed like the outcome depended completely upon her, and yet in her heart she trusted God alone to provide the answer. And did that power fall in bucketsful! Mom never in her life felt anything like what she felt that sweltering July evening.

"Suddenly, Mom spoke, her eyes round as Moon Pies. 'The heat, I feel the heat,' she said. 'Why, it is so hot! It's really burning and burning!'

"Then Julia moved her hand and gently placed it on Mom's stomach. 'Julia, your hand is hot as an iron!' she exclaimed with great excitement and overwhelming volume.

"The truth is that the power of God fell upon her in a way that literally felt like fire and Mom couldn't help but cause an uproar."

SAY WHAT?

"Dad attended that prayer meeting also. He watched as they laid hands on the sick and prayed for their healing as was the custom for years at the end of those prayer meetings. Sometimes people got better, but usually nobody much got healed, yet still they prayed. All he could make out of what she said was something about 'it is so hot' and 'hot as an iron.'

"He had no idea what she meant about 'the heat.' He thought, 'Perhaps Monica left the iron plugged in again, back at the house, and she just remembered it.'

"If she *had* left the iron plugged in, it wouldn't be her first time. The summer before, on their way to the beach for vacation, she 'bout burned down the house but remembered just in time that she had left it plugged in after ironing Dad's t-shirts and underwear. He would not wear them without that crease! Then they had to return to the house and unplug it. By the time they got back home, the iron had turned red hot. I remember Dad saying, 'That iron was hotter'n a three-dollar pistol.' I never knew how hot a three-dollar pistol got, but I guess cheap guns get hot when you fire them too much. The entire bedroom was on the verge of going up in flames with smoke pouring out of the side window. *This* night though Mom wasn't talking about leaving an iron on at the house."

MUST HAVE BEEN SOMETHING SHE ATE

"It also passed through Dad's mind that Mom's declaration about the burning may have been some indigestion kicking up. She just ate beans and onions for dinner, but then he thought, 'Surely she wouldn't be crying out about *that* in church.'

"Little did Dad know that Mom was becoming the bona fide recipient of an authentic creative miracle. God was restoring her reproductive organs, and she would soon be able to conceive.

"One thing everyone knew, Julia Skunk could sure pray down the power. That and her loving nature were what made her lingering odor bearable to the other saints at the church. Her being a skunk had certain drawbacks after all; but when you were in trouble, she could almost always pray you out of it if anyone could.

"The days soon following that powerful experience in the prayer meeting, my mom got pregnant. Now, Herb and Monica Moose, after expecting this baby for almost eight months, anxiously awaited my arrival."

COMPLICATIONS

"There had been complications since the conception of this moose. First Mom's blood pressure rocketed, threatening to jump right off the charts. Then the bleeding started. No sooner had Mom's bleeding stopped, after an all night prayer vigil led by Julia and her I-Group (Intercessing Group) as she called them, that the oncologist diagnosed Mom's cancer. Dr. James Pepper diagnosed her as having cervical cancer after a large lump had developed in Mom's lower abdomen. He reported that the tumor had grown to the size of a softball.

"Dad said it seemed to them like hell itself bared its teeth against my being born. Think about it: first Mom could not conceive then after she did, she developed two serious complications.

"Then the extraordinary kicked in. In the midst of all the anxiety and sickness, the most wonderful thing happened. With hope having evaporated like dew in the desert's noon day sun, when even Julia Skunk and the I-Group could not break this curse of cancer, the Lord did a most remarkable thing."

THEN CAME THE ANGEL

"He sent an angel; a very large one with broad wings that stretched out over ten feet. When he appeared in Mom and Dad's cracker-box sized bedroom, his huge wings spanned wall to wall. The room lit up from his presence and their eyes got big as silver dollar pancakes. I imagine they looked like two shocked owls sitting side by side on a pine branch in a world-class lightning storm. His presence ratcheted them straight up in bed, petrified with fear.

"Oddly enough, powerful winds and climatological changes accompanied this angel. Some spotted a purple tornado near our house at the approximate time the angel appeared to my parents. Then hailstones the size of golf balls fell for two minutes followed by 3.5 inches of snow that fell in less than two hours. There was some supreme head scratching going on that evening in our part of the country. To this day no one in the area knows why the weather behaved so strangely and if they heard *our* explanation for it, few would have agreed. We believe that the unusual weather pattern attended the appearance of the angel."

Peculiar Garb

"The heavenly messenger appeared dressed in a most peculiar way, not at all attired as one would expect an angel. Dad said he sported what looked to be a cream-colored letter sweater that glistened like the noonday sun. The front of it was monogrammed with the most marvelous royal blue letter 'B' trimmed in gold. When Dad fearfully eked out a question about what the letter stood for, the angel said:

'Why do you ask after my name seeing it is Beautiful?'

"The answer was similar to the response given by the angel that visited Manoah, the father of Samson, noted in the biblical account of his birth.[6] And then he disappeared in a sudden burst of brilliant light, leaving a distinct aroma of fragrant roses in the air."

The First Message

"That's not all that the angel did before he left. He gave my mom and dad a remarkable and most encouraging message:

"'Mooses!' he said, 'Almighty God sent me to tell you about your unborn boy Moose. His name is to be Theodore Conquest. At first his friends will call him Teddy. Later he shall be known as 'Mystic' for he will be one who reveals and demonstrates the power of being in relationship with the Lord His God. Mysterious aspects shall typify his friendship with the Almighty. Ere his antlers first shed he shall possess personal knowledge of his heavenly Father. He is called to be a proclaimer of Good News and have a ministry of signs and wonders revealing the available majesty of Jesus the Christ. Many will speak against him, not understanding God's calling for his life. Joyful shall he be for he shall

---

6   Judges 13:18

25

continually radiate the atmosphere of hilarity that surrounds God's great throne in the eternal throne room. As one greatly beloved of God he shall pioneer fresh pathways of faith into the supernatural experience of holiness. Mighty and mystic shall he be as one who knows he is called and beloved of the Father. At a future time, Monica, you shall be instrumental in him finding his destiny. Fear not. Now, Monica Moose, rather be healed in the matchless name of Jesus the Christ.'

"By then both my folks had stumbled out of bed and trembled in the presence of this great messenger. That is when Dad asked him his name. Then the angel, smiling a brief but quite interesting smile, touched Mom's stomach with the tip of his outstretched index finger. She felt the same kind of heat build up inside her that burned when Julia Skunk prayed down the power, only this time much, much more intense. She instantly knew she was healed. Dad fainted, fell forward to the floor, and scuffed up his brand new loafers. No one ever figured out why or how Dad put his shoes on after getting out of bed to be addressed by the angel. We know that he wasn't wearing them to bed. Mom thinks he stepped right into them when they were shook out of bed through the sheer terror of the presence of that angel. People do strange things when God moves in supernatural ways."

AN AUTHENTIC MIRACLE

"When Mom went back to Dr. Pepper, he verified her authentic miracle. Days earlier, the tumor appeared clearly on her x-ray, looking so much like a softball that the technician did a double take. After this amazing event, however, he shot another x-ray that revealed no tumor at all but just a faint spot where it appeared to have been lightly chopped away."

MYSTIC CONTINUED THE TALE

"When news of the angelic visitation and Mom's healing reached her Christian friends, major league rejoicing broke out in the First

Full Blown Holy Ghost Gospel Fellowship. The next night at their regular Wednesday evening meeting, all kinds of stuff happened, unusual stuff, wonderfully disconcerting stuff. Mom and Dad's story of the angel released so much faith and conviction, glorifying God, that forty people bolted to the altar to give their lives back to Jesus and quit their sinning. The presence of God intensified so much that half the congregation began to laugh uncontrollably while many began weeping as the presence of God began to grow and intensify. This was not the first time something like this happened among God's people. One similar event is described in the book of Psalms.

> **"When the Lord brought back the captivity of Zion, We were like those who dream. Then our mouth was filled with laughter, and our tongue with singing. Then they said among the nations, 'The Lord has done great things for them.' The Lord has done great things for us, and we are glad."** [7]

"My Momma, overwhelmed by all that transpired in the visitation, fell down in the floor and stayed there for three hours along with a large number of women, including her close friend Julia Skunk. Numerous men also fell under the power of God, including almost half the recognized leaders of the church. The power of God so touched many of the members of the church that they couldn't walk. Some tried and could crawl eight or ten feet and then drop back to the floor for a while before trying again."

REMARKABLE MIRACLES

"Other most remarkable things began to happen. One involved Julia. She was one of the finest believers in the church and much beloved. And, as you have heard, her powerful intercession on behalf

---

[7]   Psalm 126:1-3

of her friends helped many of them, but she did smell quite bad as a general rule. Remember, she *was* a skunk. However, folks in the church and in the community loved her for all of her kindnesses and her ability to pray people out of difficulty.

"She could have had an operation that would relieve her of her *odiferous* (smelly) condition, but she could not afford it. Her insurance at the Drug Store where she worked did not cover it, being a pre-existing condition when she got on there; but in the midst of the powerful move of the Spirit of God, Julia Skunk stopped smelling bad."

(Now, I know this is hard to believe but I am reporting this word for word, just as Mystic Moose related it to me in Magellan Matthew's back yard that day.)

"When Julia first got up from the floor, after quite some gargantuan effort I might add, some noticed that she began to smell differently, much like gardenias. Sometimes the fragrance is stronger than others, but that delightful fragrance of gardenias always attends her. This miracle quite bamboozled us one and all!"

'BELLOWING' BOB JOHNSON DISCOVERS GARDENIAS

"Bob Johnson, pastor of the First Full Blown Holy Ghost Gospel Fellowship and known by many of the young folks as 'Bellowing' Bob Johnson because of his loud voice, noticed the difference first. He began to smell a strong fragrance of flowers in the church that night and walked through the sanctuary looking for them. He noticed the aroma got stronger as he came to the place where Julia lay prostrate on the floor. 'Bellowing' Bob cocked his head in surprise when he realized that the sweet smell emanated from her. He used to brace himself, *olfactorily* speaking, when he got close to Julia because of how he generally experienced her to be smelling.

"'Great God Almighty,' bellowed 'Bellowing' Bob boldly, as he realized that Julia had gotten an odiferous miracle. 'This is the most

God I have ever come across. Julia has the aroma of heaven upon her. Now she is the best smelling saint in the fellowship!' That was how Julia Skunk overcame her aromatic deficit."

THEN THERE WAS IVA

"Another one of the ladies, Iva Benthinken, also experienced a miraculous deliverance. She was a bit odd in many ways but a very loyal member of the church. She was so introspective that growing up some of the neighborhood kids called her 'blinkin blinkin Iva Benthinkin.' Her spells of introspection grew worse. By the time she became an adult, her introspection caused her to blink and think, then think and blink some more before she would even answer a simple question. She had these great big round glasses that magnified her small pinpoint dark eyes. One person described her as looking like a calf wearing goggles in a tin shed during a horrific hailstorm. She made quite a sight.

"As the presence of the Lord increased during the service that night, Iva said she felt an evil presence leave her. She said that the depression that had plagued her most of her days suddenly left as she felt the evil presence depart. She sensed that the depression seemed to follow the evil presence out of the building like a dark trailing tail wind.

"'All I was doing was thinking about how marvelous it was that Jesus healed my friend Monica Moose. I've known her all my life and she just wanted to have a baby in the worst kind of way. Oh, the joy of her becoming pregnant so thrilled me, but when she was going to lose that child . . . well it just broke my heart.'

"At that she began to weep. Then she said, 'Then I saw Him! I saw a vision of Jesus. He is real. He is really, really, real! He looked so amazingly beautiful. He suddenly appeared, walking toward me. He tenderly placed His bronzed hand on my cheek and then momentarily rested it upon my head. He gently brushed back a fallen lock of hair that covered one of my eyes, just like my mother used to do in such a warm way when I was a child. I know Jesus did it that way 'cause He wanted me to be sure I saw Him with both eyes. As He touched my head, He smiled at me in a way no one else ever has. What I saw in that smile is beyond explanation. That's when the evil presence left me. I could feel it going.'"

Iva's Depression

"Iva had been plagued with depression since her daddy left her and her two sisters as orphans, just two short months after her mother died of hypertensive pneumonia. Iva, being the oldest of the sisters, felt the weight of the world fall upon her own frail shoulders that day. The pressure of caring for herself and her two sisters was much too heavy for her to bear.

"That night when she got delivered, she jumped up and down repeatedly and wound up running four full laps around the sanctuary. Each time she did she ran right up one side of the platform, between the pulpit and the preacher chairs, and then down the other side again. She almost ran over the preacher. She blew by the portly assistant pastor, Harry Sasser, so quickly that when he cut his head to follow her flight, his cheap toupee stayed still while his head turned under it ninety degrees. That humorous sight is one several of the saints will not soon forget. While his hairpiece remained aimed in a northerly direction, his head looked in a more southeasterly direction until he came to his senses and righted it. Harry was a tight Scottish gentleman who didn't mind scrimping on the quality of toupee he wore. His frugality caught up with him that night. People telling the story still chuckle when they think of him.

"Pastor 'Bellowing' Bob Johnson just shook his head at what was going on and kept muttering under his breath things like, 'Nothing like this is mentioned in the Pastor's Handbook. My seminary professors never covered in class anything about how to handle this kind of thing!'"

RUNNING FOR JOY

"On Iva's fourth and final lap, she ran right out the back door five blocks all the way home, so excited to be free that she left her old, lime green Oldsmobile in the parking lot. Her husband Ben could hear her shouting at the top of her lungs a block from their house, 'I am free! I am free! Thank You Jesus I am really, finally, completely free.' Iva's changed countenance shocked Ben when he saw her rush through the front screen door, praising God at peak volume. She motioned for him to come, cut through the kitchen, dashing full speed out the back door toward the church. He chased her all the way back down to the church, huffing and puffing the entire distance. Knowing her to be a meek and quiet soul all their days together, he needed to find out what had happened to his wife. They both came skidding back into the sanctuary together.

"He said, 'I want whatever Iva has. We have been married for twenty-five years and she is not the same woman that left for church earlier this evening. Whatever she got, I want it too.'

"When the dust settled some, they told Ben Benthinken II about the angel healing Monica Moose of cancer in Jesus name and about the vision Iva had of Jesus laying His hands on her. He thought a moment, looked and listened to all the raucous joyful bedlam goin' on in the sanctuary. With all the seriousness and conviction he could muster up he said, 'Well then I take this same Jesus for myself!' He hadn't been in church in years. Didn't see the need."

STINKING DRINKING BEN BENTHINKIN

"At that, Ben suddenly fell down under the power of God in the middle of the aisle between the pews where he had been standing. He lay there motionless for at least forty-five minutes, maybe longer. Later, he reported that it was as though he was stuck to the floor and could not move. While he was on the floor, the Lord dealt with him about some deep issues in his own life. When he got up, he knew his life was different. Iva said that when he got home, he threw away his collection of pipes, his custom-made European tobacco canister, and a hidden pile of dirty books that Iva didn't know he had. He even canceled his subscription to Playboy magazine that he had since he was a college boy. He had been getting them mailed to the office. But the best news of all was that the Lord delivered Ben from alcoholism. He had been bad to drink. Everybody in town knew it. The boys down at the high school used to get him to buy them beer on weekends. Behind his back they called him 'Stinkin Drinkin Ben Benthinkin', but no longer. He was free and glad of it."

REVIVAL FIRES SPREAD

"News of the amazing events occurring in Mom's church circulated throughout the region. For five solid weeks, night after night crowds gathered listening to the testimonies of the newly saved, helped, and healed. Room was not sufficient to hold the crowds that came. They opened the windows and people who stood outside looked through and listened. Nine hundred and seventy five people got saved the first ten days. We lost count of the ones who came back to the Lord who had tired of religion in the past. People were everywhere. Some would hang in the windows and others lined up to wait for someone to leave so they could squeeze in.

"The atmosphere was heavenly beyond description, particularly during worship. A new level of creativity emerged. Worship leaders began to write their own worship songs. Many lives were changed during those days.

"But as in many visitations of the Lord, trouble and persecution waited just around the corner. Just as the atmosphere of heaven increased in the church, so did the criticism of many. Oddly enough, the most serious opposition came from the church, not the general populace of our home town."

MIRACLE CHALLENGED

"Some of the opposition accused Mom of fabricating the serious-ness of her sickness, questioning her healing. Dr. Pepper attended an-other church several miles away that began to hear about the moving of the Spirit of God in our church. They were a part of the God Used To Do Miracles But Not Now (G.U.T.D.M.B.N.N.) denomination of churches. The complicated name of their church reflected their com-mitment to *their* form and understanding of doctrinal purity. Many of them were aggressively hostile towards our church and what was going on. Some began referring to it as 'that Crazy Cult Church.' One thing is true though, religious people (and I distinguish between truly spiritual people and religious ones) often criticize the lively activity of the Holy Spirit. For some, fear produces their criticism. For others, it is ignorance of the spiritual realm, arrogance, or lack of knowledge. For some, it is a combination of all four influences."

DR. PEPPER THREATENED

"The G.U.T.D.M.B.N.N. (God Used to Do Miracles, But Not Now) elders, led by their Pastor Dr. Ranklin Rhinoceros, Sr. told Dr. Pepper, 'You must have made a mistake about this x-ray business. God is no longer in the miracle business, hasn't been going on since they finished writing the Holy Bible. Would you not like to reconsider your conclusion on the matter of this ridiculous idea of the moose/cancer healing?' Dr. Pepper knew Dr. Rank Rhinoceros, Sr. was not asking a question. He knew the difference in an honest challenge and a threat. They exerted all kinds of pressure upon him to recant his story. They refused to believe that God had done any of the things that had been reported, but Dr. Pepper refused to bow to the pres-sure or tell a lie to agree with those who would not believe the truth concerning the healing of Monica Moose. When he first examined her, he could literally feel the tumor himself. It was large! It appeared on the x-ray. Her test proved positive for cancer; and then later, after her spiritual encounter, the cancer disappeared. End of story! He had seen it all himself. He knew it to be true. He continued to say to his critics, 'That is my story and I am sticking to it.' Later, he added one more adamant phrase to it …'so back off!'

"With a certain sadness but with great resolve, Dr. Pepper left the G.U.T.D.M.B.N.N. church because they refused to accept his expert testimony and because he refused to forsake the reality of God's power. He remarked, 'When one's mind is made up prior to the presentation of the facts, then that kind of blindness is dangerous and frightening. I can understand and even admire those who disagree with me; but when plain facts are ignored, that becomes a self-imposed blindness to reality. That I will not yield to. Wisdom Incarnate dictates that I disassociate myself from such 'blind leaders of the blind.'[8]"

BIRTH AND DEATH

"In the midst of the controversy, Mom went into labor. The morning of my birth coincided with the day that the revival began to die. The pressure of public opinion in the area increased so much that Pastor 'Bellowing' Bob Johnson discontinued the special services. His once bold bellowing receded to a mere whimpering. It was a dark day for the First Full Blown Holy Ghost Gospel Fellowship congregation. Pressure from the community and criticism led by Dr. Rank Rhinoceros' Church took its toll on a people unprepared for both the level of power and glory the Lord released as well as the intense persecution that arose against them.

"Many were disillusioned and confused, but in the midst of it all, joy abounded in the Moose household. After eleven hours of labor on November 11th, at eleven minutes after eleven a.m., an eleven pound eleven ounce fuzzyheaded moose arrived, much to the delight of my mom and dad, Herbert and Monica Moose. A son was born. I

---

8   Matthew 15:14

was their miracle baby and they knew the Lord in a much deeper and richer way through their ordeal. They named me Theodore Conquest Moose. My friends would call me Teddy.

"Later they called me Mystic Moose."

C H A P T E R   3

TEDDY MEETS THE ANGEL

Flabbergasted! Dumbfounded! Astounded! Take your pick. They accurately described my swirling mind as I sat under the old pecan tree in Magellan's backyard listening to Mystic's wild tales. I had no grid for understanding his stories, never mind the capacity to believe such nonsense. No church I ever heard of had running or crying or laughing as part of their normal services. Laughing!?! There is no laughing in religion! Just quiet contemplation or maybe occasional whispering, possibly some frowning and hymn singing, but not laughing. My limited church experiences came more from *The Lord is in His Holy Temple, let all the earth be silent before Him*" school of thought.

Whoever heard of a transformed skunk that stopped smelling bad and began to smell like gardenias because she attended some bizarre church service. Preposterous! Then there was the huge angel with a ten-foot wingspan wearing a letter sweater with a big 'B' on it. Utterly ridiculous! My head spun as I attempted to absorb the information this very strange old moose reported to me, looking at me through his tortoise shell glasses with those intense brown eyes.

Not wanting to offend Mystic Moose since I truly liked him, and yet not wanting to continue the interview, I decided to diplomatically end our association. Who would believe any of it anyway? I did not! I could not!

ANGUS' DIPLOMACY FAILS

I began, "Mystic, I am sure that you are a fine person. For a long time I have been interested in you and wanted to write about you, but your story is so bizarre that I cannot in good conscience continue. The stories about the skunk and the chief coming back from the dead, and the angel with the sweater…."

MYSTIC ANSWERS

"Angus, my dear, dear man. I know you seriously question the truthfulness of my story and that my accounts are beyond your sphere of experience. You must remember though that God has a sovereign right to do unusual things with people at different times and has done so throughout recorded biblical history.

"For example, Moses was eighty years old before God revealed Himself to him in a most unusual and supernatural way as he followed his sheep on the backside of the desert. At best, the desert is a forbidding place. How much more so its *backside*? If God's primary motivation was to appear in a palatable and normal way, the best place for Him to do so would not be in the worst part of such a forbidding place. Not many people go there. Those who do are not expecting an encounter with God.

"Then there was the form in which God revealed Himself to Moses. The Scripture says, **'and the Angel of the Lord appeared to him in a flame of fire from the midst of a bush. So he looked, and behold, the bush was burning with fire, but the bush was not consumed.'**[9]

"God spoke to him out of a dry, burning, desert bush. Even though it was on fire, it never burned up. Under normal circumstances a bush like that could not burn long. Consider the implications of a *fiery talking bush*. That makes very little sense, and yet God chose that method to reveal Himself.

"Not even in previous books of the Bible had such a thing happened, yet through courage and faith Moses opened his heart to just such an experience with God.

"Consider Moses' life experience until that time. He was born into a family of despised Jewish slaves in Egypt. Through a remarkable chain of events, the daughter of the Pharaoh, the King, adopted him into the ruling family of the world's most powerful nation. For forty years he lived a life of privilege and luxury until he murdered an Egyptian he found mistreating one of his Hebrew kinsmen. When others discovered his crime, he fled for his life, became a shepherd, and hid in an unpopulated place. For forty long years he wandered through this barren region, following his flock of sheep.

"Do you know what sheep leave behind them? That is what Moses walked through all those years. Then one day God confronted him in a way completely outside his comfort zone and his experience. He spoke to him from this burning bush to take off his shoes because he was standing on holy ground! God called 'Holy Ground' the kind of experience many would reject as not having been originated by God

---

9   Exodus 3:2

at all! Think of how much poorer Moses would have been if he had ignored that burning bush and concluded that since this encounter was far outside his experience it must be invalid.

"Nothing I told you so far is quite as inexplicable as God revealing Himself through a burning, talking bush, and yet that is the way He chose to get Moses' attention. In that peculiar manner, Jehovah initiated a process of deliverance for the enslaved Hebrew nation who had been oppressed by their Egyptian lords for four hundred years.

"Angus, please. Take time to hear me before you write me off as some kind of crackpot. My experiences with God are real, actual occurrences, and none violate the *spirit* of the Scripture. All I ask of you is that you hear me out. If, after I finish telling you my story, you're unwilling to write it, then I will accept your decision. You're under no obligation to me, but I know you are the man to write my story. Remember, you wanted to meet me for a long while. Here I am. What do you say?"

At that moment, from out of a nearby rhododendron, flew a sparkling white dove that quietly landed on Mystic's shoulder and began cooing calmly. I noticed the bird earlier in the bushes and marveled at her brilliant whiteness. The dove looked at Mystic then turned her head and looked right into my eyes. She actually made me nervous for some odd reason. Then I thought, "What kind of person possesses such quietness of spirit that a very skittish bird would land and remain on his shoulder?"

I considered Mystic's words, his logic and sincerity of heart. The dove landing on his shoulder was amazing, but I was not sure that I completely agreed with him.

Then, before I gave him an answer, he began to tell me more of his story, just as if I agreed to continue. His quiet words came with compelling power and I could not but listen to him.

MYSTIC CONTINUED

"My mother didn't tell me about the supernatural occurrences that accompanied my birth until later in my life because she knew I must have my own experience with the Lord to enter into all that He planned for me. If you think that what I told you so far is far-fetched, then you must buckle your seatbelt my good man. You have just begun to hear of the marvelous things that God has done in my life and in the lives of those I have known."

MYSTIC'S CHILDHOOD

As I listened to Mystic Moose's tales, I continued to see how unusual this man was, outwardly very calm and peaceful, but in his nature a high-energy kind of guy. He said that even as a child he was an energetic pursuer of life and became more and more of a hand-ful for his parents as he grew older. He made friends with Thelma Skunk's tenth child, Larry. Everyone called him Skunk Larry because of a humorous episode that happened in the first grade.

Although Skunk Larry was a skunk, he did not smell like one. He was born after the Holy Ghost touched his mom and she began to smell like fresh gardenias. Mystic said Skunk Larry didn't smell exactly like gardenias but didn't smell bad either. He could only deduce that the transformation his mother had somehow changed her DNA and Larry lost the stink!

FIRST GRADE

As Mystic told it, his first grade teacher, a fastidious yet fat old wal-rus named J. Hickman Dumpford, was a retired U.S. Army Colonel. (The J stood for Jasper, but he didn't want anyone to know.) By the time Teddy and Larry attended his class, Col. Dumpford dressed his rather rotund physique in pants hiked up almost beneath one of his lower chins. He was a tubby little chap who "looked as if he had been poured into his clothes and someone had forgotten to say *when!*"[10] Rumor had it that in a fit of frustration his wife Palmetto described his sloppy attire as looking like a walking bag of hammers. He sported a big drooping handlebar mustache that nearly touched his belt on both sides since his trousers were jacked up so high.

Having been mightily influenced by his years in the armed forces, he conducted all of life's activities military style, strictly by the book. Mystic said he called the roll every single day according to the military method, "last name first, first name second, second name last, no nicknames allowed." Mystic's parents named him Theodore Conquest Moose and most people called him Teddy for the first twenty years of his life, but to Col. Dumpford he was Theodore!

On the first day of school Col. Dumpford called the roll; and when he got to Mystic he said, "Moose, Theodore Conquest?" Mystic responded, "Here, sir."

Then Col. Dumpford, arriving at Larry's name, bellowed out "Skunk," hesitated a few seconds and then called, "Larry"? Larry, who was already daydreaming, didn't respond. So again the old walrus barked, "Skunk, Larry?"

Larry continued daydreaming, so Col. Dumpford bellowed one more time at the top of his lungs, "Skunk, Larry?" and then looked all around the class. He finally drew a bead on the only skunk in the class, who for the moment looked out the window, living in another world, and that of his own making. Larry, being away from home for the first time, thought his real name was 'Thweety-pie' since that's what his mom always called him at home. He hadn't connected to being called Larry, never mind Skunk Larry!

---

10   Quote from P.G. Wodehouse

Young Teddy Moose could not contain himself for some strange reason and began laughing hysterically at the sound of Larry's name spoken in just such a way, especially by this odd looking teacher, whose BB sized eyes rolled back and forth in his huge old head as he looked around the room identifying each new student. From that day on, young Teddy and all his friends called Larry 'Skunk Larry' (when they didn't call him 'Thweety-pie'). Teddy and Larry spent the next thirty minutes standing in a corner, each on one leg with a book balanced on their heads as punishment, Larry for daydreaming and Teddy for "unauthorized laughing in class." Teddy learned that it was easier for a skunk to balance a book on his head than it was for a moose because of the cranial substructure of the moose's noggin. His book kept falling off, extending his time of punishment.

BRAVER THAN NORMAL ANIMAL SCOUTS

In the third grade, Skunk Larry and young Teddy Moose became charter members of the new Scout patrol, the "Braver Than Normal Animal Scouts." Accumulating merit badges became their passion. By the spring of his tenth year, young Teddy prepared himself to qualify for his "Courage and Bravery" badge, the most important level of attainment one might achieve, especially if you pursued leadership of the "Braver Than Normal Animal Scouts" troop. To earn this badge each member must spend two consecutive nights in the woods alone, build a camp with a lean-to type shelter for sleeping, and find and cook one's own food. Each scout could only take with him a "Braver Than Normal Animal Scouts" official manual, a flashlight, a waterproof container of matches, a roll of string, a sleeping bag, a blue tarp, some slats for a lean-to, and the official Swiss Army pocket knife -the Animal Scouts purple model with all twelve blades (not to mention the toothpick and tweezers), a supply of hot dogs, a bag of marshmallows, and the clothes on one's back.

THE CHALLENGE: BEING ALONE

Since he never slept alone in the woods before, young Teddy became apprehensive. The more he pondered this challenge, the more he realized he'd never been alone that long before, *anywhere*. One would think with him being a moose, and having come from a long line of moose, that sleeping outdoors would not be a problem, but he was a third generation domesticated and "bi-footular" moose (walked upright on two feet like most other folks). Bottom line, young Teddy did not look forward to sleeping outside in the elements, especially alone.

DAY ONE

According to Mystic Moose, he spent his first day building his shelter, the required lean-to that should protect him from the weather. When nightfall came and all the strange sounds began, the temptation to bag the excursion and go home rose in his heart like an ever-encroaching ocean tide. Skunk Larry and the rest of the gang were trying to win this badge as well, and Teddy could not let himself be the only one who "chickened out." If he quit, they might start calling *him* 'Thweety-pie' instead of Larry. Why, even his pal Livingstone C. Pigeon was going for his courage and bravery badge, and he was *related* to chickens, for goodness sake. How would it look for a moose to "chicken out" when the closest thing to a chicken in the whole troop didn't? Allie Gator was going for his badge too. He would never hear the end of his harping if he didn't "man up" and stick it out.

Teddy built a campfire and began to roast hot dogs and cook a few marshmallows. He liked to catch his marshmallows on fire, then blow them out and eat them with the burnt part still on 'em. Finally, he crawled into his "Goes Down to Zero" model sleeping bag and prepared to retire, but sleep eluded him as the reality of spending the night alone for the first time in his entire short life began to settle upon him. Accompanied only by his thoughts, a strange sense of anticipation began to unnerve him. He could not shake an uneasy sense that crept upon his soul like the long early evening shadows of summertime when days eased into nights. Lying flat on his back in his sleeping bag, gazing into the stars, he began to question some things for the first time ever.

THE QUESTIONS BEGIN

"Who made those stars? How far away are they? What is outer space? Does space ever end? If it does end, what's at the end?"

In Natural Science class, Colonel Dumpford explained that there are 50 billion galaxies having millions of stars just like our sun. In class the vastness of the universe didn't impress him at all. He accepted the Colonel's teaching on the universe as facts to be learned to pass a test, but now they became a frightening reality as the hugeness of space impressed him.

"How could there be so many?"

"Who put them there?"

He remembered other things the Colonel taught about light, the distance to the sun, and the huge distances found in space. As odd a fellow as the Colonel was, young Teddy realized he was a great teacher. The Colonel taught that light travels at 186,000 miles each second and that it takes eight minutes to travel from the sun to earth. Teddy was not sure how fast 186,000 miles per second really was, but he knew he had never gone that fast himself, even on the roller coaster "Lightening Bolt" when he lost his hat and sunglasses from the speed.

The longer he considered the reality of the heavens, the more frightened he became. Before, the nighttime sky looked one dimensional, like a flat black sheet with holes punched in it with a light bulb behind making the holes look like stars. Now for the first time, Teddy knew that space was real and the stars were far, far away, but how far? Each question seemed to resonate into an endless eternity that Teddy had hardly considered before.

He began to experience fear, a strange new kind he never knew before. It was much different than the fear he felt when that mouse ran up his pajama leg last year at summer camp. That fear ended after it jumped out the other leg and Livingston grabbed it and flushed it down the toilet. It was not even like the fear he had when the snake got inside his shoe in the closet last spring. This fear seemed to ring from eternity past through the present into an unending future. Yet it was not a natural fear at all but one causing him to have a deep appreciation for everything he saw and knew. It was as though no matter what direction he looked or thought, there was no end to time, space, or anything.

WHAT ABOUT ME?

Teddy next wondered about himself. "Where did I come from? Why am I here? What am I supposed to do with my life?"

Then his thoughts turned in another direction. He began to wonder about God.

"Who is God?"

"Is the God that mom and dad told me about real, or is that just some kind of fairy tale? What does He look like? I've never seen Him."

Overwhelmed with these sudden new questions, this strange other-worldly kind of fear began to steal quietly but aggressively over his soul. He decided to fall asleep to quiet these strange new thoughts of time, space, and eternity, but sleep did not come easily for the young moose that night.

He said out loud to no one in particular, "Dude, I guess you really do need courage and bravery to win this badge."

Finally, after much tossing and turning in his brand new sleeping bag, he allowed his imagination to kick into gear to block out the questions and the fears.

To avoid these thoughts, Teddy Moose began to imagine playing baseball, his favorite sport, and being with his best friends, Skunk Larry and Livingstone "Carrier" Pigeon. Finally, he fell asleep.

Day Two at the Campsite

Teddy's next conscious moment began with the chirping birds, then the rising of the sun. When fully awake, he knew that life was different than when he first entered these woods and that it would never again be the same.

An Unusual Presence

The second day of Teddy's camping trip, he captured and classified butterflies, collected and identified leaves and other plants. He concentrated on concentrating, trying to keep his mind from wandering back to the uneasy night before. Being alone was very difficult for him. Until these few days, he never realized how much he filled up his life with meaningless things. Now he wondered if it was to avoid some of these very thoughts. He also considered the night that lay ahead. A sense of dread began to fall upon his ten-year-old consciousness like a fine mist upon a meadow. Teddy was not so confident about staying in the woods another night alone. All day he felt a strange uneasiness, as though someone was watching him, or that some unusual presence was nearby.

By nightfall Teddy began to feel relieved knowing that by morning, if he actually stayed through the night, he would be the proud owner of the coveted "Courage and Bravery" badge. It was his final badge and would make him one of the first scouts to complete all the requirements. He hoped to become the very first den captain of the Braver Than Normal Animal Scout Troop. He hoped that Skunk Larry and his other friends would pass this test as well.

TEDDY CONTINUED

"I can still remember the abundant sounds of the forest that evening as the crickets chirped and the katydids sang their vibrant song. The comforting sound of the cooing field doves soothed my soul."

Teddy began piling the dry wood he gathered earlier in the day, opened the official Animal Scouts "Always Dry" canister of matches and began a roaring fire with his final match. He was already out of hot dogs and the marshmallows had lost their appeal, but Teddy had smuggled some baloney into several pairs of socks in his knapsack. The scoutmaster hadn't discovered his hidden contraband delicacy during the pre-campout inspection. He skewered them on a small tree branch and began roasting them over the open flickering flames.

"Nothing quite satisfies a man's soul like wood-fired fried baloney, one of life's special pleasures," he said to himself.

Even though he was not supposed to have anything extra with him on this outing, he knew he could not do without baloney for two straight days of serious "living off the land" type Courage and Bravery level camping.

THE NIGHT FALLS

Night's ebony curtain descended upon the young and restless one, having never felt so alone in all his moose life. Teddy could not remember a night so dark and air so still. Thank God for the chirping crickets. They were his sole company. Only the flickering flames of his roaring campfire broke the shroud of darkness. Heat from the flames warmed him, and the baloney would be ready to consume any minute. Teddy settled into the last phase of his Animal Scout's challenge facing his fears, ready to overcome all obstacles.

Suddenly, the nighttime's normal forest sounds turned to eerie silence. Then the hair on the back of Teddy's neck stood on end as he instinctively sensed a marked change in the atmosphere surrounding his campsite. Teddy's antlers also began to vibrate slightly, an innate warning sign most moose experience when danger is near.

A *SUDDENLY* OCCURS

His heart began pounding so hard he felt it throbbing in his stomach. Then from out of nowhere, a brilliant light flashed and radiated from behind him. At first he thought someone turned on one of those brilliant revolving spotlights they had at grand openings of theatres or a new car dealership. The light was so bright that his fire dimmed in comparison. As he turned around to identify the source of the light, Teddy's first thought was, "Oh no, they found out about my illegal baloney. They have come to disqualify me from garnering my Courage and Bravery badge."

When Teddy Moose turned around, there before him stood a giant angel, brilliant in his countenance. He held an extraordinarily large sword whose glistening blade seemed capable of dividing time from eternity. He was dressed most peculiarly. He wore a brilliant white letter sweater with a heavenly blue colored "B" on it.

Never more terrified in his life, Teddy tried screaming, but at first nothing came out. Finally, he made some highly inarticulate kind of terror stricken guttural sounds. Once he caught his breath, he screamed for real at the top of his lungs, took two desperate lunging steps forward and dove headlong, antlers first, through the evergreen branches of his homemade lean-to and under the blue tarp. He scratched and clawed his way forward under his "Goes Down To Zero" brand sleeping bag. (It was the special model that actually had an antler shaped zippered enclosure to warm the heads of scouts who needed such.)

Teddy shook uncontrollably.

"Surely this has nothing to do with contraband baloney," he thought.

THE ANGEL SPEAKS

"Theodore Conquest Moose!" commanded the angel. "Come out and stand before me."

Although scared half to death, Teddy found himself crawling out from under the sleeping bag. There he was on all fours, looking straight at the kneecap of a twelve-foot angel. Teddy felt abnormally weak, unable to stand to face this dread being.

"Arise young moose!" spoke the angel.

Although Teddy had no strength of his own, he found himself rising and standing before this awesome being. His knees knocked together like two Mexican castanets. He trembled so much that his antlers began to vibrate, making a high-pitched whirring sound, sort of like a hummingbird's wings do while feeding.

Then the angel said in the most majestic comforting tone, "Do not be afraid, young Theodore, for the Lord has sent me to tell you His grand purpose for your life. You are called to preach the everlasting good news of the grace of God to many people in many places. As you proclaim the grand message of Christ Jesus, supernatural occurrences shall follow and healings will be multiplied. You shall influence a great number of young people as they find new life in the Lord Himself."

TEDDY RETREATS

Whereupon young Theodore Conquest Moose once again dove antlers first burrowing under the lean-to hollering for all he was worth, ignoring completely the angel's suggestion to not be afraid. The mighty angel reached down, grabbed Teddy by the ankle, and pulled him out of the lean-to. Teddy hung upside down, high in the air staring intently into the angel's face. Then the angel flipped him effortlessly around in midair and he slowly descended, light as a feather, until he landed on his feet before him. Teddy was staring wide eyed at the heavenly being wearing the sparkling letter sweater with the marvelous blue letter 'B'.

THE ANGEL CONTINUED

"Furthermore young moose, I hereby commit you to the word of the Eternal God's great grace. Now, kneel before me to receive your calling!" Teddy kneeled as commanded.

The angel extended the massive silver shining sword touching young Teddy first on one shoulder, then the other shoulder, and finally, the top of his head. Then the awesome heavenly creature smiled the most marvelous loving smile, walked over into the campfire and disappeared upwards in a spiral of smoke.

Teddy fainted.

MYSTIC MUSES

"The next morning I woke up exactly where I had fallen," Mystic Moose added. "At first I was unsure if the events of the prior evening actually happened or if I dreamed them. I had difficulty thinking clearly.

"The whole experience seemed unreal. I vacillated between wondering if an angel did visit me or if I had some kind of strange dream. My mind raced from event to event as I tried to remember the angel's words. Could it be true that a moose like me could be authorized to see people healed by the power of what the angel called the "everlasting good news of the grace of God?" What did the angel mean that supernatural occurrences would follow?"

ME, A PREACHER?

Teddy was not really interested in being a preacher. So far, his experiences with church were boring and confusing. He did not know any preacher that had any kind of fun on a regular basis. He wanted to be a musician, form a band with Skunk Larry, Livingstone Pigeon, and that new kid in town, Allie Gator. Allie already had a bass guitar. He had been telling them about the band his brother was in and how much fun they had traveling and playing. Besides, a lot of the good-looking girls at the high school had a real attraction for the guys in Allie's brother's band. They were called the "Moon Dogs." None of them *were* dogs, but names of bands needed to be cool, not accurate.

Livingstone, Larry, and Teddy already earned their musical merit badges in the Braver Than Normal Animal Scouts. They planned to form a band when they could afford some instruments. They were convinced they would hit the big time when they got into high school, could pool their resources, buy a bus once they got their driver's licenses, and hit the road playing music every weekend.

Teddy already had a guitar, and could play seven chords pretty well and another four on occasion. Livingstone was taking piano lessons from Nelson Spivey's mom, the local music teacher from the high school. Skunk Larry was a whale of a drummer, but neither of them had their own instruments yet. Larry took drumsticks with him everywhere he went and beat on everything not nailed down. He got in trouble in school twice for beating on his desk, once in shop class and another time in French class. He was a tapping fanatic. He would beat his sticks on the walls and lockers at school as they walked from class to class, on his friends heads in front of him as he walked, and on the table in the cafeteria when they ate. Larry was almost out of control, but he was dedicated and he had rhythm. All of them had the vision to be a band.

Now as Teddy fully awoke, he realized he was not in his sleeping bag but on the ground covered with dew near the now cold campfire. He lay exactly where he fell when he fainted the night before. His damaged lean-to truly confirmed the angelic visitation of the night before. The memory of two panic driven dives through it was quite real, but he had never heard of a moose having a divine call, never mind one his age. All he was trying to do was win his final merit badge in the B T N A Scouts.

The events of the previous evening involving the angelic visitation and the dubbing of the sword seemed surreal. Then Teddy noticed on his shoulder a gold colored dust. Looking on his other shoulder, he found some there too. A breeze began to blow and Teddy felt a strange sensation on the top of his head, like after visiting the barbershop when your new haircut feels different. So he reached up and touched the top of his head directly between his two young antlers. When he brought his hand down, he had some of his own hair in his hand, neatly and uniformly clipped as though cleanly cut by a very sharp blade. He had his very first "flat top." Teddy remembered the shining blade of the sword the marvelous angel had wielded. He remembered its sharpness and that it seemed as though it could divide time from eternity. Teddy concluded then that he had been literally visited by an angelic messenger from God. His head was filled with wonder. His heart began to feel a strange new sensation. He could only describe it in later life as a mixture of resolve and faith. He knew that his future had a divine destiny and that it was imperative for him to follow it.

His First Short Prayer

He prayed for the first time in his young life, "Lord, if You want me to do the stuff that angel told me, then I will do so with all of my heart. Let me know what You want me to do and when You want me to do it, and I will give it my best shot."

Teddy's Conclusion

"When I finally concluded that the angel really had come, I knew I was keeping this bizarre episode a secret. Who would believe me anyway! I had some great friends, but I was seriously hesitant to tell them about the angel and what happened that night in the woods."

"Time to pack up!" Teddy said aloud to no one in particular. With that he rolled up his sleeping bag, gobbled down his last remaining marshmallow, and waited for Col. J. Hickman Dumpford to pick him up and confirm that he won his badge of honor.

CHAPTER 4

THE POWER OF FRIENDSHIP

As Angus scribbled furiously to capture every word, Mystic continued to tell him stories of his formative years and the friends he made. In order to capture more completely this incredible tale, Angus brought his tape recorder. With his remarkable gift of recall, Mystic remembered long ago events and specific conversations with amazing clarity and detail.

As you know, Angus was very hesitant to continue listening and writing the stories that Mystic told him because they were so different from his understanding of normal Christian experiences. Angus was constantly amazed and often perplexed by Mystic's bizarre yet lively stories. Half the time he could scarcely believe what he was hearing. Yet he realized that the very process of listening gave to him a tremendous feeling of new life, and hope arose in him in a most mysterious and unexpected way. He did not understand how that worked but was grateful. Since the death of his wife, neither hope nor joy seemed to be viable alternatives for him.

MYSTIC CONTINUES

"My young mind reeled from the mysterious supernatural events of that final night of my quest for the Courage and Bravery badge," said Mystic. "The next morning Colonel Dumpford picked me up in his antique 1926 black Model T pickup. By the time he found me, Livingstone, Skunk Larry, and Allie Gator sat sprawled out in the beat up bed of the truck.

"Livingstone blabbed his head off, his mouth going a mile a minute, while Allie Gator, with his eyes drooping at half-mast, almost nodded off. Only the lurching of the Colonel's old truck kept him awake. Skunk Larry looked like he had seen a ghost. I had never seen him look that pale. He would not look me in the eyes for more than a second. I decided to wait until later to ask him about his week-end in the woods. I didn't feel like talking about mine either. I was plenty spooked.

"Each of us successfully completed all requirements to get our merit badge for bravery. Livingstone bragged about some poor pitiful little snake he killed. Hearing him tell it, you might conclude that he narrowly escaped the fangs of a twenty-foot python. One would think that *this* pigeon sitting in the back of the Colonel's pickup was the world's most courageous of all birds, but then pigeons were afraid of snakes no matter how green or small.

"I thought to myself, 'All of us needed to be brave these last few days, but *some of us* needed to be braver than others.' Of this I am sure, as I relived the big scary angel holding me upside down!"

THE AWARD CEREMONY

"At the award ceremony the next Tuesday evening our whole gang sat at the head table with Col. Dumpford. The old Colonel presented quite a pretty picture in his Scout Masters edition flat brimmed Royal Canadian Mounted Police style hat and olive green knickers with red knee socks. He decided that particular *look* best suited his unique physique and was the best choice of all the uniform styles available for Scout leaders. He looked quite dashing, or as dashing as any fat overweight walrus/former Army Colonel could, who hiked his pants up to just about his chin while his long droopy mustache hung almost to his belt.

"'He is proud of us though,' I thought. I was proud of my crew too. During the dinner and prior to the awarding of the Courage and Bravery badges, I looked at my three closest friends and thought, 'I sure love these guys. Whoever believed that a moose, a skunk, an alligator, and a pigeon could be so close? Friends for life, that's what we are. We must endeavor to let nothing separate us, ever!'"

SKUNK LARRY, TEDDY'S CLOSEST FRIEND

Skunk Larry was Mystic's best childhood friend. Over the years they proved the truth of the adage: "*The firmest friendships have been formed in mutual adversity, as iron is most strongly united by the fiercest flame.*"[11] They were inseparable, made for adversity, adventure, and excitement. When none was available, they made some up.

As a child, Skunk Larry contracted scarlet fever. In those days antibiotics were not as available for treatment, and so the MD watched the condition closely. Dr. Pepper told Larry's folks that he needed to monitor his blood daily for a number of weeks. Each afternoon little Larry, accompanied by Teddy, would trudge down to the Dr.'s office which sat at the end of their street across from the grocery store. Day

11   Charles Caleb Colton

by day they entered the office full of trepidation. In those days MDs drew blood samples from people's fingertips using pointed blue steel razor blades. Skunk Larry dreaded the thought. His fingertips hurt so much when Dr. Pepper's nurse, Wilma Waddelle, poked a hole in them to draw the blood. Teddy thought she seemed to enjoy doing it way too much.

"Just watching it hurt me more than it did Larry, and it hurt him stupendously!" Mystic said. "So, one Saturday morning I devised a plan to end the entire painful prolonged process. In my young mind, engaging in a form of guerilla warfare with the local medical profession proved to be our only option. At least that was how I viewed it at the time.

"Back then, on Saturday mornings the area farmers came to town to pick up supplies and do their trading, some in old pickup trucks but many of them driving their mule drawn wagons. Most of them parked at the hardware store, across the street from the medical office. The grocery store sat next door where they bought their weekly provisions. It was customary for many of them to stand by the curb, catch up on the news, chew tobacco, scratch occasionally, and spit some. They smoked their Saturday cigars and threw the butts in the gutter when they were finished. Meanwhile, their waiting mules would bray occasionally and deposit manure piles in the road behind them, as mules are apt to do."

A Plan Emerges

As the impending medical appointment drew closer, Teddy knew the painful process would begin all over again.

"Teddy," Larry said, "I can't keep doing this. My fingers are so sore, all the way to the bone, almost every single one!" And then he began to sob.

How often Teddy sat out front in the waiting room, listening to Larry's muffled sobs as time and again the nurse pricked his sore fingers to draw blood. That Saturday morning the proverbial light bulb of genius switched on in Teddy's young mind as he stood on the curb watching the farmers wander into town one after another, their wagons drawn by their smelly braying mule teams.

Looking at Skunk Larry's fingers, then across the street to the Dr.'s office, and then back to the mules standing in the road, his anger began to boil.

A PLAN COMES TOGETHER

"Enough is enough!" Teddy blurted out loud to no one in particular.

He grabbed Skunk Larry by the arm, and the two of them went into the grocery store and begged two brown paper sacks from Ralph Beason, the bag boy. Then easing outside, Teddy began loading up his sack with all the old cigarette and cigar butts he could find, mixing in some fresh mule manure. Larry had no idea what Teddy was up to but sensing it was important, began doing the same with his sack. After both sacks were sufficiently loaded, Teddy proclaimed boldly, "Follow me, Skunk Larry. We are going to put an end to the heartless and continual poking of your fingers by the medical profession!"

"How?" Larry asked, mystified.

"With the well placed contents of these sacks. That's how!" Teddy said. "Skunky ole boy, follow me. I love it when a plan comes together! Your days of pain filled finger pricking are rapidly drawing to a close."

At that, Teddy bolted across the street, and stealthily eased up the stairs to Dr. Pepper's waiting room. He thought the room was empty; but actually, Nurse Waddelle, also the receptionist, was in the dark far corner leaning down into the shadows re-arranging the magazines in the wooden wall mounted rack. Grinning confidently from ear to ear with great anticipation of victory, Teddy eased open the screen door barely making a sound. He knew beyond a shadow of a doubt that sabotaging the waiting room of the Dr.'s office would somehow end Skunk Larry's painful treatment. That could only make sense to a young moose desperate to help his suffering best friend.

Without hesitation Teddy dumped his sack of cigar butts on the floor and slung the remaining mule manure all over the top of it. Then he grabbed Skunk Larry's bag and dumped it on top of that. Both of them peered into the waiting room with great joy, admiring their work. This would fix the medical profession once and for all. They had been warned:

"You've been messin' with the wrong Moose and Skunk!"

THE HASTY RETREAT

The two boys scrambled out of the waiting room towards the front steps when in a flash the sun broke through the clouds and into the waiting room. From the corner of his eye, Teddy spotted Miss Wilma slowly emerging from behind the magazine rack resplendent in her brilliant white sun-splashed nursing uniform.

She took one step out into the slick "no man's land" of cigar butts and fresh mule manure, instantly slipping into the pungent mire. As she began her decline into the gruesome quagmire, as a last ditch effort she grabbed whatever she could to keep from falling. In desperation one hand grasped the wall-hung magazine rack which instantly pulled out of the dusty plaster and crashed down around her throwing printed matter everywhere. When Miss Wilma hit the deck, she cut loose with a bloodcurdling scream, sprawling and clawing wildly in the nasty debris left by the two boys.

WILMA WADDLES IN PURSUIT

Wilma slipped and double dipped, struggling to her feet, then finally lunged toward the front door in pursuit of the Moose and Skunk. By now "the Old Waddler" as Teddy used to call her, was covered from head to toe in the residue of mule manure and cigar butts. As the result of her slippery demise, she also had pages from the current *Time Magazine* firmly plastered to her notable hindquarters. Teddy's surprise attack had so frightened her that she turned pale as a ghost.

Covered and strewn about with assorted debris, she rushed forward toward the screen door as she spotted the two scrambling boys dashing frantically around the corner of the office building for all they were worth. She looked a lot like an enraged bull elephant in a nurse's cap and whites, but the screen door refused to yield to her hurried advance. In her panic she ran right through the screen, breaking the door apart in the intensity of her adrenaline/anger infused rampage.

She charged through the door jamb like a berserk bull moose looming up through the weeds of some remote Alaskan wilderness and bellowed at the top of her lungs as the two perpetrators escaped to safety.

"Teddy Moose, I will have your hide for this. You just wait until your daddy hears about this! "

The two boys ran across the vacant lot back behind Teddy's Aunt Kathryn's house and hid in her barn in the hay bale fort they built earlier in the year. Sitting there as the flush of victory began to fade, Skunk Larry began to realize the implications of their guerilla attack.

THEIR LATE RECONSIDERATION

"This doesn't look like it's going to end that well, Teddy!" Larry whispered as both of them peeked out of the barn window, straining to see any possible approaching authority figures.

"And how were all those cigar butts and mule manure going to get me out of the finger pricking anyway? That was a dumb idea."

"Well, it seemed like the best plan at the time," Teddy offered. "What were you going to do anyway? Let them punch all your fingers black and blue and then let them start on your toes?"

Teddy picked up one of Larry's hands and declared, holding one of his bruised fingertips, "As far as I'm concerned, I will not let them get a hold of one more of these again! If they try, we will take our warfare to the next level. *Moose and Skunk* shall strike again with fierce wrath and reckless abandon!"

Larry did not *even* want to know what the *next level* might be and received very little comfort from Teddy's confidence. He knew he meant business though and so valued his best friend. Sometimes his ideas were crazy, but Larry did admire this moose's spunk. He remembered a proverb his mom quoted to help him identify what a real friend looked like. She said, **"A friend loves at all times, and a brother is born for adversity."**[12]

"Teddy and I were friends like that, and boy, had our times suddenly become adverse all because of Teddy's wild plans!" Skunk Larry thought.

BRUISED FOR *THEIR* INIQUITIES

Not much later that day, irate fathers Herbert Moose and Wendell R. Skunk flushed both boys out of hiding and gave them the spanking of their young lives. About mid-flogging, both of them easily questioned the logic of their earlier actions. Teddy knew what they had done was wrong, but when Dr. Pepper concluded it was not absolutely necessary to prick Larry's fingers on a daily basis, he was relieved for Larry's sake. Teddy did not mind the spanking so much for two reasons, the first one being that he had stuck some cardboard in his shorts before the spanking to soften the blows. And secondly, he knew that his friend wouldn't continue to suffer, even though they had to apologize to Dr. Pepper and face the wrath of Miss Wilma "the waddler" Waddelle and clean up the mess they made.

When it was all said and done, Teddy and Skunk Larry concluded between themselves that even if they failed to stop the daily pricking

---

12   Proverbs 17:17

of his fingers, it was almost worth the whipping to see Miss Wilma rolling around on the floor amongst the cigar butts and fresh mule manure. Never had they seen a more uproarious sight than her crashing through the broken screen door with all the debris stuck to her white uniform. She'd never looked finer! After all, decisive action must be taken to preserve the welfare of your friends. True friends are worth facing any danger, even an enraged female member of the esteemed medical profession.

PLAYING TOGETHER

This episode only strengthened the bonds of friendship between Teddy and Larry. Playing sports together did as well. Both of them loved athletics of all kinds and could almost always be found playing some kind of ball. In the fall you found them playing football with the rest of the neighborhood boys in the front yard of Aunt Kathryn's two-story white clapboard house, between the two monstrous magnolia trees.

On many wintertime weekends they sneaked in the high school gym to play basketball. Of course, the gym was locked all weekend, but the boys were small enough to squeeze in through one of the side windows; and one of the area high school stars, Stanley Lane, did it too and sometimes let them in. He was a real gym rat, came from a pretty rough part of town, but could shoot the daylights out of a basketball and loved to play. One night, Teddy and Larry were walking home from Allie's house by the high school when they heard a ball bouncing in the gym, but the lights weren't on. When they peeked in they saw old Stanley, riding a skateboard, dribbling his basketball, and smoking a cigar. They thought that was one of the craziest sights they had ever seen. Even at their age they knew the cigar couldn't be a key to his prowess on the court, but maybe being able to dribble while riding a skateboard was.

In the summertime, they played baseball for hours with the guys at the park. Their dads coached some of the local youth athletic teams.

Teddy and Larry came from a long line of athletes. Skunk Larry's dad was one of the top outfielders in those parts. At first he was one of the region's best catchers, but the umpires demanded he change positions. The fumes that arose from Wendell Skunk as he manned that position inhibited the umps' ability to call balls and strikes from behind him at home plate. Air circulation was better in the outfield where Wendell proved to be one of the county's best players ever.

THE CAPTAINS

Teddy was a born leader. He demonstrated his skills when he talked poor Larry into the fiasco he concocted at Dr. Pepper's office. He was frequently chosen to be captain of the teams he played on. When Teddy and Skunk Larry were seniors in high school, Teddy was elected captain of the football team. They won every game except one, but Teddy felt empty in the midst of his success. He knew that Larry wanted to be captain of a team too but had never been chosen. So when basketball season rolled around, Teddy privately asked all the other members to elect Larry captain. Teddy would gladly give up being captain just to see the look on the skunk's face when he got the news.

The elections for captain of the basketball team yielded co-captains for the first time ever, Skunk Larry and Teddy Moose. Only after many years did Larry discover how it happened. Until then it remained Teddy's secret. He knew it was the right thing to do. Larry was his best friend.

Teddy's mom often told him that the Lord would provide him with friends if he proved to be a friend to others. More than once she quoted him this proverb: **"A man who has friends must himself be friendly, but there is a friend who sticks closer than a brother."**[13] Teddy proved his friendship over and over and discovered in Skunk Larry a friend who did stick closer than a brother. Who would ever imagine that a skunk and a moose could be such tight friends!

---

13   Proverbs 18:24

LEARNING TO FORGIVE

Some of the adversity that brothers are born for is created through the very closeness of their friendship. Spend enough time with anyone and eventually, you will have some kind of disagreement.

Most boys fight with each other. Some believe that this aggressive behavior is wrong, but in truth it is a facet of the developing male personality. Apart from a father's discipline it can become dangerous; nevertheless, the development of the male's aggressive nature is necessary. Men need to be aggressive to provide for and protect their families and to secure their personal destinies.

Teddy Moose and Skunk Larry were no different than other kids. They usually got along well with each other, but when Larry's brother Lamar was around, skirmishes abounded. Lamar was three years older than either Teddy or Larry and always knew how to stimulate hostility between them. He had a good buddy named Bart Friday who had a lot more character than Lamar but liked the kind of misadventure Lamar created wherever he went. Lamar believed it was both his duty and calling to do so. He had a sixth sense that enabled him to cause controversy and release potential disaster into their very midst. Once Lamar came close to ending the tight friendship Teddy and Skunk Larry enjoyed.

As young boys, one of their favorite places to play was a large sand pile at the bottom of the hill below the Skunk family's house. On hot summer days Larry and Teddy would play there for hours, only taking short breaks for relatively unimportant things like lunch or personal relief.

On one such morning Lamar saw his brother and Teddy enjoying the sand pile with all of their trucks, army men, and other action figures. He said to himself, "The time is right to stir me up some trouble …as in Larry-Teddy conflict." Lamar and Bart joined them in the fun at the sand pile, but when neither one was watching, he asked

Bart to distract Teddy and Skunk Larry for a moment. Bart distracted the two friends while Lamar hid Teddy's favorite G.I. Joe action figure in his pocket, the one with the kung-foo grip that every kid wanted but very few had. Lamar always wanted that toy and so comprised a plan to obtain Teddy's for himself.

After a while Lamar eased over to Teddy and whispered in his ear, "Did you know that Larry stole your favorite G.I. Joe? You know, the one with the kung-foo grip?"

Devious Lamar planned this caper for several days. Earlier, he casually informed his brother Larry that Teddy had lost his G.I. Joe, could not afford another one, and was going to try and trick him into buying him a new one.

Skunk Larry looked up from the sand pile and noticed Teddy eyeing him suspiciously. Teddy started to circle him, sizing him up.

"Larry, where's my G.I. Joe? It was here a minute ago and now it is gone!"

"How should I know where it is, Teddy?" Larry said.

At that point Lamar looked at Teddy, raising his eyebrows in a way that said, "Larry's lying," and shrugged his shoulders.

"I know you took it Larry. I can see it in your eyes. You are lying to me! Now fork over the G.I. Joe with the kung-foo grip."

That did it. Skunk Larry turned and ran towards Teddy, diving headlong into him, knocking him down. Before you knew it, fists were flailing, sand and fur were flying, and Lamar was howling with delight. All you could see was a brown, black and white whirling collage of Teddy's antlers and Larry's flashing tail. As the two boys rolled around in the sand fighting, Lamar howled with laughter. (Bart looked on in shocked unbelief. He did not know what Lamar was up to.)

THE THIEF REVEALED

As Lamar doubled over with laughter, the pilfered G. I. Joe figure squeezed out of his pocket, falling at his feet in plain sight of everyone. Lamar's eyes got big as saucers. He knew his dastardly deed had been discovered. He took off running, but his feet moved so fast that all they did was dig a hole beneath him with sand flying out behind him in a stream. The two fighting friends realized that Lamar suckered them both. Teddy and Skunk Larry grabbed hold of him as his traction-less feet were spinning. Then all three of them were fighting.

Several of the young Skunk sisters arrived on the scene, attracted by the flurry of fists and flying sand. They immediately screamed, "Momma, Momma, you better get out here fast. The fur's a flyin. Larry's got a black eye, Teddy's got a busted lip, and Lamar's face just turned deep purple cause Larry's got him round the neck. Teddy's chewing on his ankle and won't let go."

"Lamar T. Skunk! Larry Skunk! Stop that fighting this instant or I will turn the water hose on the whole bunch of you!" shouted the matriarch of the whole Skunk clan. "Look at you hooligans. Why, you've almost destroyed the sand pile!"

Then she snatched hold of Lamar by his ear and Larry by the ankle, shook them real good, and drug them out of the tussling pile of boys. Teddy was so startled that he came to himself rolling and grasping at the air as he continued fighting and swinging in vain, yet there was no one left to grab or smack.

"Go home, Teddy, and tell your Momma exactly how poorly you behaved," she demanded. Teddy did not want to go home. By now he was ashamed of himself. He began shuffling around kicking at the sand with a sheepish look on his face.

"Get to stepping!" she barked as she poked a shaking bony finger in the direction of Teddy's house. Teddy turned for home and took off running.

By now Teddy's lip was beginning to swell and his elbow was bleeding where he banged it on a yellow metal Tonka Toy dump trunk in the sand pile during the fight. What troubled him more than the pain was realizing that Lamar had tricked him into fighting with Larry. How could this have happened? What would they do now? They had never been at odds with each other before, not like this. Teddy feared it could be the end of their friendship.

CROSSING THE STREET

John Pressley was the neighborhood druggist and owned Pressley's Drug and Soda Fountain. The store sat right across the street from Teddy's house. He and Larry spent many an afternoon after school and some Saturday mornings sitting in the booths at Dr. John's, drinking chocolate shakes, chewing Bazooka bubble gum, blowing bubbles, planning adventures, and reading comic books.

The boys grew up crossing the street together going to the store. The candy counter and the soda fountain were part of the fabric of their lives. Teddy first met Larry at that candy rack looking at packs of Topps baseball cards. They both had a habit of picking up a pack and smelling it real good before making their purchase. Neither could remember life before the drugstore hanging out there together and sitting in the booths with many other friends. Its wood floor, whirling ceiling fan, and gleaming stainless steel and chrome soda fountain set the atmosphere for many happy memories.

Later that sweltering summer afternoon, Teddy peered out his front door. Across the street stood his oldest friend Skunk Larry, looking into the drugstore window. Teddy knew that he was actually looking for him in the reflection of the front door of his house. Teddy felt so bad about the fight. Larry *had been* his best friend.

Mystic said, "As a kid, if I stood and looked just right into the drugstore window, I could see Larry's front door in the reflection. If he stood there, he could see mine too just next door. Whenever we had a fight, both of us knew where to go. If you stood there long enough, sooner or later you would be spotted and see the other one coming over."

It became the place that Larry and Teddy reconnected after fighting with each other. If they didn't do it there, they would reconnect back at the sand pile. Both places became their personal "forgiveness" places.

"How could I let Lamar separate me from Skunk Larry?" Teddy wondered. "He never stole from me or lied to me before. Why was I so willing to believe he had now? By golly, I *am* glad Larry squeezed Lamar's neck until he turned purple. Why, I would like to grab him by the throat right now myself."

Teddy pulled open the front door to his house and slowly made his way to the drugstore. Larry could see him in the reflection of the store window as he walked through the yard and across the street to Pressley's Drug Store. As he approached his friend, Larry quietly said without turning around to face him, "Sorry, Teddy, *my* bad!"

By now both boys' eyes were a little moist cast down looking at their feet. Teddy shuffled the toe of his shoe around in the sand beside the sidewalk, nervously kicking at a non-existent pebble.

"I am sorry too, Larry," Teddy said. "It was never your fault. I should have trusted you instead of accusing you. Friends?"

"Yes, best friends!" responded Larry.

Both boys learned a valuable lesson that day: never receive an accusation against one another. Ask one another the kind of questions that can unravel any disagreement. Then be quick to forgive and realize how everyone is so prone to making mistakes and capable of doing the wrong thing.

Mystic Draws Some Conclusions for Angus

Mystic stopped speaking for a moment, and then said, "Angus, as a child we used to recite the Lord's prayer at the end of every church service. I remember one little boy who said part of it this way, 'and forgive us our *trash passes*, as we forgive those who *passed trash* against us.' Now what the Bible says and what he should have said was, 'and forgive us our trespasses as we forgive those who trespass against us,' but in all honesty he touched a vital truth. Many people pass along trash about other people's lives and produce unnecessary strife. All of us have 'passed some trash' at one time or another. The trouble is that since all of us have some trash of our own, God will not forgive us as long as we continue to pass along other people's trash. I have known some who have remained in a state of condemnation and oppression because they constantly criticized other people. God will not release any of us from that oppression as long as we continue to gossip. One of Satan's chief methods of destroying lives and relationships is by gossip or passing trash.

"Years later, a remarkable British preacher emphatically declared to me in his broad Northumberland brogue, 'Mystic, if God did not forgive, heaven would be empty. What a lonely place an empty heaven would be!'

"Angus, how true that is. God wants to be with His created ones. He does not want to be alone either. The book of Genesis reveals that He took great delight in walking with Adam in the garden. When Adam fell from his place of great friendship with God, He already knew that it would take the death of His dear Son Jesus to bridge that dreadful chasm. As a child, I knew that I did not want to be alone and discovered that it would take acts of forgiveness at times for friends to stay together."

WHAT EVERYONE NEEDS

"Angus, everyone needs a sand pile and a drugstore window. As a child, that was the place I began learning forgiveness. I continued to discover the importance of forgiveness in a much deeper way later in my life. It is one of the keys that has kept me close to God.

"God made His Son to be like that drugstore window and yet much more. He became for us the Place of Forgiveness. When we look into His life, we see reflected there the great love of the Father who yearns to reconcile men to one another and to Himself. It was enough for me that Larry and I were friends once more. He was the best one I ever had. I have often said, 'Who would ever believe that a skunk and a moose could be best friends!?'"

FELLOWSHIP DEEPENED

"Skunk Larry and I came dangerously close to losing our child-hood friendship in the conflict Lamar instigated. Our reunion and forgiveness made us closer than ever. It not only helped us understand one another, it also uncovered our own inclination to mistrust and accuse one another. Through that episode, I realized Skunk Larry and I had more in common than I knew. Our experience with Lamar and the massive fight we got into happened the summer after we earned our Courage and Bravery badges in the Braver Than Normal Animal Scouts.

"I remembered the ashen look on Larry's face the morning Colonel Dumpford picked us up after our final night in the woods. I was too shaken to discuss anything that had happened. I didn't want to ask Larry about why he looked so frightened in the truck that day either. Then, I just wanted to keep moving.

"But now seemed the time to ask him about it."

REVISITING THE ANGELIC ENCOUNTER

"Larry, do you remember the trip back after our last night in the woods when the four of us were pursuing our Courage and Bravery Merit badges?"

"Remember?" Larry said. "I have tried as hard as all 'get out' to forget it, Teddy."

Mystic Moosetales: Redefining Wildlife

Skunk Larry hesitated. He was at a personal crossroads. If he never talked with Teddy about that night, he would be forever irresponsible for what he knew to be true.

SKUNK LARRY CONTINUES

"I saw what happened to you that night in the woods! I saw the angel, or whatever it was. I heard what he said to you. I even saw him pick you up and spin you around in midair. You floated down slowly in the air, just like a feather wafting in the breeze."

"You saw that?" Teddy exclaimed suddenly.

"Yes," continued Skunk Larry. "I was walking through the woods trying to find you that last night because I had this peculiar fear I had never experienced before. I knew that if I could talk to you a while, I would feel better and could finish my night in the woods and win my badge. You remember how dark it was that night? As I looked for you through the woods, I suddenly saw a bright light turn on and headed over to it. That's when I saw you and the angel.

"Yes, I saw the sword. I saw the angel. I saw the heavenly blue colored letter "B" on his brilliant white sweater. I heard you scream too. I heard the things the angel said to you about what God wants you to do in the future. I saw you dive back into your lean-to, and I saw the angel pull you back out and touch you with his awesome sword. It was when your antlers made that humming noise and your knees were knocking loudly that I lost it. I knew if you were scared then, I sure was too. I fainted and fell right back into a sticker bush.

"Teddy, this is the first time I mentioned this to anybody. I have been afraid to even think of it."

"Me too, Larry. The experience was so troubling that at times I awaken in the night and begin feeling like that angel is near, or at least it feels something like it did when he first appeared, only not so intense."

"Teddy, that is not all that happened to me that night. When I regained consciousness, that same angel was standing over me and called me by name. When I arose with great trembling and stood before him, his eyes were like burning flames. He spoke with a voice that sounded like the Niagara Falls in its roaring."

"Well, what did he say to you, Larry? What on earth did he say to you?"

"He told me that I was called. He said that we were to work together in what he called 'His special service' before the foundation of the world was created (whatever that means???). He said that many need to hear the message of the gospel or their lives will be lost forever. He said many who are sick do not need to be and that Jesus would use us to help get them healed.

"Teddy, do you think that means we are supposed to be doctors like Dr. Pepper? He also told me that we would meet others in the future who would help us, train and inspire us, and some who would misunderstand us and 'try' us with their evil intentions and actions. He promised me that if we would trust the Lord all the time, we would never fail. Then he smiled at me such a smile as I have never seen before and disappeared, poof …in a puff of smoke and vapors.

"Teddy, what does all of this mean?"

"I don't know, Larry, but whenever I think about it, I have the sensation of sitting on a roller coaster pulling that seat belt snug. You know that feeling, don't you? Sort of glad to be on board but with your stomach creeping up into your throat, a bit afraid of what lies ahead."

Teddy and Skunk Larry looked at one another for a few moments. Teddy shrugged his shoulders in a sort of "gosh, who can tell what it all means" kind of way. Then he grabbed Skunk Larry wrapping both arms around him and lifted him off his feet, gave him a hug, and then put him down.

Teddy looked through the big storefront window at the soda fountain.

"Let's get a milkshake!" Teddy suddenly exclaimed.

"At least one apiece, maybe even a couple, some Bazooka bubble gum too," replied the happy skunk. They entered Pressley's drugstore once again but this time as fast friends forever!

CHAPTER 5

THEN
THERE WAS
CHURCH

As the days became weeks, Mystic Moose regained strength. In a mysterious way, over time his own testimonies revitalized him. I watched him transform before me as his face took on a countenance of light. Around him I felt some kind of atmosphere or bubble of life. He articulated his episodes so well that sometimes I felt as though I was experiencing them as I heard them.

A strange thing happened to me as I listened and recorded his tales. My depression, that dark emotional cloud that enveloped me since the death of my wife Marilyn, began to recede. I began to feel a kind of vibrant hope; that's the closest I can come to defining the force that began lifting my spirits. Yes, hope began dispelling the blanket of depression. The time I spent with Mystic became a restorer of my life.

He had something I longed for. I just didn't know exactly what it was or how to get it, but I wanted it.

As he grew stronger, we frequented the large park in the center of Lincolnshire where we often continued my ongoing interview. Lincolnshire, S.C., the town where Magellan and I live, has a thirty-five acre park dedicated to seventeen local young men who gave their lives during World War II. Most of them died in the Battle of the Bulge as paratroopers in the 101st Airborne. In the center of the wooded acres lies a lake, set like a sparkling diamond in a blanket of verdant green foliage. The morning mist rises in the early hours to give it an otherworldly quality that I can still picture in my mind's eye. Mystic liked walking in those early morning hours. Many times we arrived early enough to awaken the dawn. Often the fog enshrouded the water like a gray opaque grave cloth. We absorbed the beauty of the sun's rays burning through the rolling morning fog as it gradually vanished and the entire scene resurrected before us. I shall always treasure those early mornings with him.

On one particular morning, Mystic told me of his early church experiences. He was the least critical, most positive person I ever met; but to help me appreciate the challenges and frustrations he faced, and to encourage others who have had similar experiences, he spoke very pointedly. Not one to mince words, Mystic knew that it was important to include in my book accurate, honest examples for the sake of truthfulness. The church had alienated many whom God called, and he knew that without understanding their experiences and becoming a vital part of a local church expression, they would never fulfill their purpose.

THE RADIANT GLORIOUS WOMAN

"Angus, early in my ministry I had an amazing encounter with the Lord. I was awakened early one morning by the force of a startling vision, one that impressed me so deeply I have never forgotten it. The first

76

thing I remembered was being in a very dark place. Fog and dreariness were everywhere. I had a terrible sense of foreboding. Then, suddenly through the shrouded mist I saw a figure approach. It was faint at first but I could tell it was someone who seemed to be on fire. As the figure drew closer, I realized that it was a woman. She was not on fire, but she had a radiance and beauty that I had never seen before. At first I thought she was some kind of spiritual being. You know, Angus, the Bible records a number of different kinds of spiritual beings.

"As the woman drew closer, the fog began dissipating and the sense of foreboding diminished until it was completely gone. I saw her clearly. She was not some spirit at all but the most radiantly beautiful woman I had ever seen. Her skin was clear as crystal; her eyes, a sparkling azure blue set off by her welcoming smile. Her hair was golden and fell in soft curls around her shoulders. She was clothed in a pure white garment embroidered with precious stones arrayed in an amazing pattern. Her countenance was so glorious that I shielded my eyes. I could scarcely look at her. When I did look she glanced back and blushed. Her cheeks flushed adding a rosy hue to her perfect complexion. She radiated an aura of innocence.

"I couldn't look at her long. I had to turn away because her countenance was so brilliant. I could not stop looking back at her because of her beauty and wholesomeness. Upon her head, shimmering in a bright luminescence was a sparkling crown shaped like a laurel wreath. Yet it shone like the seven-colored rainbow.

"Angus, she turned to leave and I cried out to her, 'Please stay.'

"As she turned back and smiled at me, my heart melted. At the same time I was filled with an amazing hope that abides in me to this day. I had a strange sense that she was a long lost member of my family and marveled that I didn't recognize her. I wondered to myself, 'Who is this glorious woman?' As though she heard my unspoken question, she said but one short phrase in a voice that sounded like a rippling stream, *'I am Church, I shall be bride.'* Then she was gone.

"'Church!?' I said to myself. 'What? How? Oh, my!'

"Then suddenly, the Lord Jesus stood before me. He radiated a light so brilliant that I could barely look at Him. Although radiant, He only wore a cloth wrapped around His waist that hung down just below His knees. I saw His wounds. They weren't really scars but open healed wounds. Through the holes in His hands and from the one in His side, rays of blinding light shone out. My knees buckled and I fell at His feet. Such a One I had never seen before.

"This is what He said to me: *'Love her, care for her. Suffer for her. I did and she is Mine. See what she will become!'*

"And the vision ended."

MYSTIC'S LOVE FOR THE CHURCH

"Angus, I have never recovered from the vision I had of that woman. The words the Lord spoke to me also showed me how much He loves the church no matter what condition it's in now. I am committed to seeing her become all Jesus wants her to be. I am deeply convinced that no one will find his or her ultimate destiny without being personally involved in the life of a living congregation."

ANGUS OPENS UP

"I never much liked church," I spoke honestly.

"Nor did I," Mystic responded. "The tales my mom told me of how the power of God transformed her church before I was born intrigued me. All of that changed by the time I knew what going to church was all about. When I was growing up, church wore me out," Mystic said as he reflected on events from many years ago.

Then he smiled in a way that betrayed his more mischievous side. When I saw that look on his face, I knew he was about to launch headlong into one of his memorable tales. I paid close attention to every word!

Mystic Continues

"B O R I N G . . . Angus!" Mystic stretched out the "boring" for a long second and looked intently into my eyes as he said it.

"Watching paint dry fascinated me more than a lot of the church I experienced when I was younger. A salt salesman trying to make a living in a colony of slugs could not have been more bored than me. As I got older, I invented creative exercises to stir up excitement. I knew church was not supposed to be that way! One of my close buddies as a kid was a carrier pigeon named Livingstone. We called him L-Stone for short. I've known him my whole life. That was as close as we could get to saying his name when we were young kids. So it stuck. He and I concocted a unique way to invigorate one particularly boring church meeting. Honestly, I did most of the concocting. L-Stone assisted and provided needed moral support."

The Year of the 'Great Flood'

"'Livingstone!' I leaned over and whispered one day in church. (I used his full name to get his attention, sort of like my folks used to do to me when I was in trouble!) 'Do you want to see a huge commotion? I am talking about a concerted conflagration of folks dashing about madly! I know how to make these deacons scramble like billy goats at a head butting contest.'

"L-Stone stared at me blankly as the two of us sat while the visiting speaker, Pastor Timotheus Stumper, droned on about the Egyptians, the Israelites, and the Red Sea. I could tell by the look in my young pigeon's eyes that he had already 'glazed' over from abject boredom himself. He was more bored than I was, if possible.

"I almost had to crack him upside the head to get him out of his dull comatose condition. Finally, he snapped out of it and said, 'I'm in. Who wouldn't want to see that?' When Livingstone got hyper-level excited, he would blink his eyes one at a time repeatedly, maybe three times. Maybe that was a pigeon thing. I don't know. Weird, but I never knew anyone else who did that. It was a sure-fire sign that he was ready for action. That, I did know.

"'Let's simonize our watches and prepare for battle!' (I meant synchronize but we were only eight years old, well anyway...)

"Meet me in the bathroom in approximately three minutes, ready for action," I instructed.

"Livingstone and I slipped out of our pews one at a time at the pre-determined interval. I waited for him nervously out in the hallway. When he emerged, we eased toward the men's bathroom situated directly across from the side entrance to the sanctuary. Just before we entered the facility, I grabbed several small paper drinking cups from the water fountain out in the hall, crammed them in my pocket, and casually strolled into the bathroom. I set Livingstone as guard by the door. Looking quickly under all three doors, I inspected each stall to ensure we were alone. With no feet visible below the doors, I discerned we were ready for action.

"'Teddy, what does going into this bathroom have to do with causing a commotion in the church?' Livingston asked as he peeked out the partially cracked door to see if any impending authority figures were approaching.

"I smiled slyly and replied, 'Hey man, check this out.'

"Angus, in our sleepy little town with not much to do we grew up manufacturing our own excitement. I remember when JayJay Marks got mad at one of his professors at the small local college. In the middle of the night, he and his cousin Bobby Sludge led a cow up on the third floor of old Warrenton Hall education building and parked that old bawling bovine in his classroom. Next day the powers that be discovered that the cow wouldn't walk back down those same three flights of stairs. At one point they thought they might have to get Marvin Felder up there to carve her up. He was the town butcher. It would have been: *live cow went up, flank steak, rib eye, and spare ribs came down.* Finally, the college decided to remove a window and rented a crane to get him out. Never underestimate the ingenuity of those guarding the bastions of higher education! The cow did leave his mark though before his spectacular departure. Academia calls it manure!

"But back to the story at hand. So then I filled the cups with toilet paper, dropped them into the commodes, mashed them to the bottom with the handle of a nearby plumber's helper, and flushed a few good times."

THE VENTURE PROGRESSED

"'Pigeon,' I said, admiring my work, 'observe some of the finer points of raising a ruckus in ye ole steeple house. One more additional flush or two of this commode by the next unsuspecting user/flushers, the tide will rise and this flood will be in full genesis. We will be long gone, never found responsible for the ensuing deluge, perhaps of biblical proportions. The first great flood won't have anything on us! Noah's Ark part II here we come. I predict that in no less than ten minutes time, the water will cross the hallway, seep into the sanctuary under the side door, and before our very eyes, deacons, elders, and other men of rank and authority will be running from everywhere trying to stem the "over-flushed" tide. We'll have ringside seats and will it be awesome? Yes it will!'

"With that brief explanation I turned and flushed the commode a few more times for good measure, and we beat a hasty retreat back into the unsuspecting meeting still in progress. With one eyebrow raised the appropriate height, Mom cast a suspicious and wary glance at me as I sat down next to her in the pew. L-Stone and I returned together. I instantly discerned that to be a tactical blunder. She was *always* suspicious of our corporate ventures to the facilities.

"As Timotheus Stumper reached maximum elocution level about Moses leading the children of Israel across the Red Sea, from under the side door rolled a relatively pristine freshly flushed tide of water from the men's room. Just moments earlier, Bob Peavey had flushed and was standing in the men's room when the waters started rolling, and roll they did, big time! He was readjusting his hairpiece and beginning to re-snap the brass closures on his suspenders, those ugly fat red ones, when he noticed the rising water level surging behind him. As he dashed out of the room in front of the advancing tide, one dragging suspender got caught on the doorframe. The hung-up suspender and ensuing tension of it ultimately caused him to lose his balance. Momentarily, that snagged suspender held him in a state of virtual *suspended* (no pun intended) animation. He leaned forward way off balance for a few brief moments that seemed like a medium eternity. When the *suspended* suspender suddenly snapped, it released its grip on him. His forward thrust caused him to trip through the doorway. With his arms flailing like an out of control windmill, he stumbled headlong across the hallway, falling forward through the swinging double doors into the sanctuary just ahead of the rising tide of water. About that time, he landed face first with a thud in the main aisle of the sanctuary, the loose elastic suspender having fully released from the doorframe.

"With a life all its own, the suspender leaped forward like a rebellious slingshot into the sanctuary, one end still attached to poor old Bob's trousers. It promptly popped Esther Ludchukker's new Sunday hat right off her head. Simultaneously, ole Bob's poorly adjusted hairpiece flipped up off his bald noggin landing on top of dear Esther's chapeau. That would be the electric blue hat she was sporting, the one with the silver objects dangling down off the brim. To us kids her hat looked like what we termed a UFO, an 'Unidentifiable Female Object'. When the ladies wore those hats to church, it reminded me of a Star Trek convention, spaceships everywhere.

"The hat/UFO with Bob Peavey's hairpiece on it landed in the lap of a man known to me only as Brother Pile, a quiet goodhearted gentleman. He had been quietly snoring his way through Timotheus Stumper's crossing of the Red Sea message. When it landed in his lap, his eyes popped open with a start. He saw this strange looking object sitting there on him with what appeared to be some kind of dead rat on top of it. When he fully awakened and saw what was sitting in his lap, he cut loose with a frightened high-pitched scream that sounded like a wounded honey badger in heat. His scream finished off T. Stumper's message for real. Stumper was stumped and trumped, but L-Stone and I were pumped!"

THE ENSUING PANDEMONIUM

"'I've been hit,' shouted Brother Pile to no one in particular as he awakened from his deep contemplation. (At first I didn't understand why he shouted that. I learned later he said that it came as a flashback from something that happened to him while he served in the Great War many years earlier.) The landing *hat-rat/UFO* startled him so badly that he jumped straight up out of his seat. His frightened shout startled a number of the smaller children in the service. They began crying as bedlam spread through the congregation. Those present began turning to investigate the source of all the upheaval. Brother Pile's reaction to these shocking events so embarrassed him that he spun on his heels and hurried out the back of the church, only pausing long enough to snatch up the hairpiece and plant it back on Bob Peavey's naked noggin as he passed him by. Imagine Brother Pile having that much presence of mind in such a state of shock. Amazing was it not? He was the type of man who demonstrated remarkable kindness even under the most extraordinary circumstances. I appreciate a man like that!"

AUTHORITY FIGURES RUSH INTO ACTION

"Just as I predicted, several of the deacons on call that Sunday saw the encroaching flood and bolted for the men's room. The mood of the moment and the zest on the morning message had been pretty well squelched. Pastor Stumper reluctantly concluded, and rightly so, that the crossing of the Red Sea would of necessity be continued at a later date. I leaned over to Livingstone and whispered with a great sense of satisfaction: 'Moses himself could not have delivered the children of Israel from all this commotion.'

"After the powers that be capitulated in the face of the flood and the meeting ended, I looked over at Livingstone and with real delight said, 'Now that is what I call having church. That worked better than my wildest dreams!'"

MYSTIC EXPLAINS

"Obviously, Angus, what Livingstone and I did was wrong, but at such a ripe young age utter boredom compelled me! Over my years of knowing the Lord, I have discovered Him to be the most exciting and creative person in the universe. Getting to know Him and walking in faith is the most exciting way to live. The Creator is the originator of enthusiasm and incalculable creativity. Yet many churches exceed boredom. Children grow up believing that God is this austere, exacting, and extremely bland person. No wonder so many young ones fall into the clutches of the evil one. He seduces them with promises of excitement, adventure, and fun, and then leads them to captivity and destruction. All of the Lord's churches should have atmospheres of excitement and creativity, maybe not in the way Livingston and I exacted, but exciting nonetheless!"

APPREHENDED ONCE AGAIN

"By the way, Angus, I got seriously caught for that prank. The Bible plainly states, *'and be sure your sin will find you out.'* [14]Mine found me out in a hurry and in a big way! If you thought the fiasco

---

14   Numbers 32:23

in Dr. Pepper's office resulted in a blistering, you should have been there for the 'rod of correction drives out the foolishness of youth' whupping I got when my folks discovered the parties responsible for the deluge and ensuing collateral damage!"

KEEP YOUR EYES ON JESUS

Mystic helped me differentiate between the goodness of the Lord and the inequities often found in the church world. He also taught me that one of God's purposes for church was to learn how to love in just such circumstances.

"Keep your eyes on Jesus, Angus," he often said, "rather than the people around you, and you will not be sidetracked into bitterness and criticism."

WHO DO YOU TRUST?

"Trusting in the church is not the same thing as trusting in the Lord! Satan, the enemy of our souls, has trapped many in despair and bitterness by keeping them focused on the affairs of the church, on what has happened to them at the hands of other believers. We can't continue seeing things from the dark side. God's heart is for us to become part of the solution, not part of the problem. Anyone can identify problems and criticize. A friend of mine used to say, 'Any jackass can kick down a barn, but it takes a wise master builder to construct one.' Our real challenge is to provide solutions."

LEARNING MYSTIC'S WAYS

I quickly learned that this Moose only talked about things when he was ready. When he began, he would suddenly introduce a topic, relating event after event, including both teaching and valuable commentary. Sometimes it seemed to me that he was rambling about unrelated things, but as I patiently listened I began to understand the importance of each part and how they related to one another. He wanted me to understand so I could articulate his insights and practical wisdom clearly to help prepare and protect the emerging generation.

MYSTIC CONTINUES

"Angus!" Mystic said.

"Yes, my friend." His tone of voice indicated the importance of what he was about to say. I needed to pay very close attention.

"I never wanted to be a preacher. I wanted to be a musician, but God had different plans for my life. In my early years I struggled greatly with His plan for my life, but now I'm so grateful He reached me. I never cease to be amazed at the power selfish ambition has to blind us to what we need. How important it is to trust God! Father knows best! Many times He asked me to do things I did not want to do. Sometimes I thought His directions were absolutely wrong for me. Over time without exception I discovered His plan to be exactly what I needed. No matter how painful or scary the thing is the Lord asks us to do, every obedience has our own welfare built into it. Obeying Him always resulted in my joy, although I was often convinced at first that I would be miserable doing it. Even Jesus' suffering was with the hope of great benefit at the end of it. The apostle Paul described Jesus' great sacrifice this way:

> **"Looking unto Jesus, the author and finisher of our faith, who <u>for the joy that was set before Him</u> endured the cross, despising the shame, and has sat down at the right hand of the throne of God."[15]**

"Yes, from my history with the Lord I learned to delight in His will, although many times I did so in almost blind faith with very little initial joy."

---

15   Hebrews 12:2

EVERYONE'S PURPOSE

"Every follower of Jesus is called to ministry. When you become a believer, you are born a second time, a spiritual birth. You get to start over. You are born into God's royal family, giving you the privilege and responsibility to live as a king and priest in the world. As a priest you have a purpose and a duty to serve and care for people, and as a king you are to reign in your appointed sphere of influence. You are appointed to rule over problems and challenges rather than live under them. The Lord wants us to increase in both serving and exercising authority in this life. Never forget that. Write that down!"

A COMMON MISUNDERSTANDING

"Too many believers think ministry is only for professionals. They misunderstand their own calling in the workplace, the home, and in society. So many people who don't know the Lord won't enter a church building. Someone on the job needs to show them love and help them. The Lord has provided tools for every believer to use in the marketplace daily to enable them to effectively live and serve those around them. The Bible calls these tools 'gifts of the Spirit,' and they include prophecy, words of knowledge, evangelism. Our failure to effectively use these tools and weapons in society is part of the reason our nation is in such moral decline.

"Sure, some will become fully engaged in the work of ministry and receive support from it (and rightly so), but they are still servants, not some special class to be treated as lords over God's household. They should be honored for their service. The Lord wants us to show true respect; but, remember, the Bible teaches us to honor every man. God values every single life in every culture."

Then the tenor of the conversation began to change.

"Angus, even with the supernatural experiences that my mother and father had and the one I had with the angel as a child in the

Animal Scouts, I did not want to be in ministry. I had other ideas of what to do with my life."

"How could you refuse after the kind of angelic visitation you had? I don't understand," Angus asked.

"Well…" Mystic's words trailed off as he considered how to answer the question.

"First of all, I didn't understand the plan God had for my life, and I was terrified by the supernatural experience when the angel visited me as a child. My first impulse, and a very strong one, was to put all of that out of my mind. The second reason was that I didn't want to be a preacher or a missionary. I thought that if you accepted God's 'call' on your life it meant you had to be one of those two."

MUSIC, MY FIRST LOVE

"I loved music and I wanted to be a rock and roll musician in a great band. As a child growing up, I knew that was one way to get attention, meet girls, and become rich and famous. As self-serving and vision-less as that was, I must be honest and say that *was* my dream. My friends and I planned our band for years. Sometimes the Lord has a real job to do to convince us to follow Him in the specifics of His calling, but more about that later."

MYSTIC CONTINUED

"So, Angus, I had two hurdles to overcome to fully follow the Lord: my own will and my experience in the church. Ultimately, I had no use for church. Not only was it boring and confusing, but to me it was painful. As a young moose, I would almost rather have a tooth pulled than sit through those boring services. I had a lot to overcome from the things that happened there, not just to me, but to my family."

Angus Questions

"Mystic, if the church is such an important part of a Christian's life, then why is it so difficult for many people?"

"Angus, the fact that church is important is the very reason that it is often a difficult experience. Satan's resistance to dynamic church life is an indication of its vital importance. And people's misunderstandings and personal desires can make it a complicated and imposing challenge."

Unrealistic Expectations, Desire for Prominence

"People can bring unrealistic expectations when they come to church. Some look for a kind of approval and security from other believers that only the Lord can give. When they expect to gain their primary inner satisfaction from their relationships with other believers, they are disappointed when this is unsuccessful. Others look for an unhealthy place of recognition. Others have an inaccurate understanding of who they are and are hurt when they are not received as they expect to be."

The Truth About Honor

"Honor is a tricky thing. When people seek it, it's wrong; but when they don't give it, that's just as wrong. Jesus said that seeking honor from men instead of from God will destroy your faith: **'How can you believe, who receive (take) honor from one another, and do not seek the honor that comes from the only God?'**[16] If Jesus doesn't know how you can believe under those circumstances, then you just can't!

"On the other hand, one must be quick to honor and appreciate other people. The Bible teaches that we should be quick to honor God the Father, the Son Christ Jesus, and the Holy Spirit. We should

---

16   John 5:44

also honor our mothers and fathers, the first commandment with a promise. The Bible also teaches to honor widows, those who serve diligently in the church, our employers, secular authorities, even all people. Angus, we should appreciate and show honor to everyone."

THE ENEMY'S SCHEME

"One of the schemes of the Devil is to embitter believers against the church. He fuels their disappointments and criticisms to separate them from other believers and ultimately, from God's purpose for their lives. A believer's life purpose is restricted and sometimes completely aborted relative to the degree that criticism and bitterness take root in their lives. If the enemy can keep people separated from one another and separated from their spiritual destiny, which is a reason for church in the first place, then the Devil knows he has them beaten."

A GREAT DELUSION

"A great delusion has fallen upon this generation. Many believe that they can find their destiny apart from true relational church life. It just isn't so. John the Apostle wrote: **'If someone says, "I love God," and hates his brother, he is a liar; for he who does not love his brother whom he has seen, how can he love God whom he has not seen?'**[17] Paul taught that to be a believer is to be part of a body, the body of Christ. How long does any part of your body live after it has been severed?

"Paul said that we should not be ignorant of the enemy's schemes. One of his basic plans is this very one, to keep people from gathering together as a church. The writer of the book of Hebrews said, **'And let us consider one another in order to stir up love and good works, not forsaking the assembling of ourselves together, as is the manner of some, but exhorting one another, and so much the**

---

17   1 John 4:20

more as you see the Day approaching.'[18] Jesus Himself emphasized the importance and power of gathering together in His name. **'Still further, I tell you truly, if two of you on earth agree about anything for which you are praying, they will receive it from my Father who is in heaven. For where two or three have met in my name, I too am there with them.'**[19]

"Another aspect of the Devil's schemes is to ruin the lives of children whose parents are in full-time ministry. God's highest purpose for a person is often accomplished through a strong relationship with his natural family. Many PK's, preacher's kids, rebel because of pressure to be perfect role models in the church and because of demonic attacks upon families who have huge destinies."

A Conflicted Moose

Mystic continued, "Angus, even though church was boring, it seemed like it was very important to go; but growing up I had trouble understanding exactly why. I was a very conflicted young Moose. It was obvious that my parents were serious about going. As I got older my mother told me stories of how this supernatural God healed and delivered her and that my birth was the result of His miraculous intervention, all of which occurred in her church. She told me that without the encouragement of Skunk Larry's mom, she wouldn't have made it and I might not have been born.

"From time to time she explained to me that the church was God's house, making sure I understood that He really lived in the people, and that *they*, not the building, were the real church but that the buildings were where *the church* came to worship and learn about Him together. But as a child I was confused. If the church was God's house, people and all, why was He never home when *we* came?

---

18   Hebrews 10:24-25
19   Matthew 18:19-20 Barclay's Translation

"It reminded me of the time Wally Bear's family moved into another house a couple of blocks away. The only problem was they forgot to tell him they were moving, and when he came home from school, they weren't there. No one was. The house was empty. It took a couple of days, but finally, they found each other. For a while Wally wandered from my house and back to his old one, each time hoping his folks to be home. He just couldn't quite figure out the part about the missing furniture. Finally, they realized that one of their seventeen kids was missing and started searching for him until they found him at my house. Things were further complicated because Wally was one of three triplets and they never could keep up with all three of them anyway. He'd rather have stayed with us in any case because food was more readily available where I lived. If you showed up late for supper in Wally's house or blinked at the dinner table, you didn't get much to eat."

FLASHBACK TO TEDDY'S YOUTH

"Still, even with my mother's explanations, I thought it odd that God never seemed to be home when we visited 'His house' each week.

"Who would continue to visit someone if the person you visited was never home? People talked about Him as though He were there, but I had never seen Him.

"I also knew that a couple of big chairs were kept up front on the platform that were scarcely ever sat in. One week all of them were filled and I thought that one sitting there may have been the Lord, but then I heard him introduced as a guest speaker. I knew that if he were a guest then this could not be his house. And after listening to him for a while, I knew that guy was definitely not the Lord."

RELIGION HURTS PEOPLE

"Things that happen to children in church can mark them for a long time. Kids are deeply affected by disappointments. I remember what happened to Harrison Braswell when he went to Sunday School on his birthday, with great anticipation, mind you. His Sunday School teacher told him that if he would come on his birthday, the whole class would celebrate it with him; he just needed to bring one penny for each year of his age. When the time came, little Harrison brought his seven pennies to church ready to party. For days he anticipated this event with great delight. When he got there, the teacher had a cake on the table in the middle of the room. However, the closer little Harrison looked at the cake, the more he realized that it was fake, made of white plastic that looked like a cake, only it had a slot in the top of it.

"The teacher put one lit candle on the cake and asked young Harrison to come forward to put his seven pennies in the slot in the cake and blow out the candle. After he put his money in the cake and blew out the candle, the class sang 'Happy Birthday' and the party was over; only Harrison was seven cents poorer. He can still remember the plinking sound of his little pennies dropping into the big empty plastic cake, one after another. I watched his face as the episode proceeded. He was so disappointed. Heck, I was too, and it wasn't even my birthday!

"When he asked if he could have his pennies back, the teacher explained that they were part of the offering being sent to feed some poor hungry kids in China.

"Harrison told her later, 'How could they be any poorer than us? We're the ones with a plastic cake.' When she frowned at him, he knew he should probably just keep quiet and kiss those pennies good-bye.

"This little event may not mean much to an adult; but to Harrison, it was a disappointment that linked his heart to a church that promises one thing but delivers another. Years later Harrison told me that as he grew up, he considered the church to be a plastic imitation at best. It was not until he was married and in the midst of a tremendous crisis that he cried out to the Lord and truly met Christ Jesus. His wife was pregnant with twins and their doctor warned him that they could lose both of them.

"In a state of desperation he went to a restaurant with a friend of his to a meeting for businessmen, the Full Gospel Businessmen's Fellowship. He had been to church all his life but never really knew the Lord. In that restaurant he responded to an opportunity to receive Jesus as his Savior for the first time. Several others came forward also. Harrison told me that when he and others went forward for prayer, one of them actually vomited on his shoe, a very auspicious and memorable altar call for sure! He said he really never felt anything special at the time and the vomiting certainly didn't help, but suddenly his life really began to change, especially when the twins were born safely although the delivery was especially difficult for his wife, Laura. The doctor said it was miraculous that the two boys were healthy. One twin's umbilical cord was wrapped around the throat of the other twin, almost killing him during the delivery. From Harrison's perspective, he met the Lord *in spite of* what happened in the church he attended."

MYSTIC'S PURPLE ANTLERS

"When I was fourteen, I dyed my antlers purple. One Sunday as I was coming up the steps to the church, one of the elders met me there and told me that I would have to dye my antlers back to their normal color or I was not welcome.

"'You are a terrible witness to the other young people in this congregation,' he said.

"He was mostly bald himself. He had a terrible comb over. You know what I mean. To cover his bald spot he combed hair way over from behind one ear to the other side of his head. On a windy day he looked like a house with a loose shingle flapping in the breeze. I told him that if he would cut that shingle off the top of his head, I would dye my antlers back. He didn't see the humor. Matter off fact he turned red in the face and muttered something under his breath. I was shocked by his response, but to be honest, part of the reason I dyed them was to shake things up. Nevertheless, the leader's remarks stung me and stayed with me for a long time. In my immaturity I resented his reaction, and my words betrayed my bad attitude. I decided that was the last time I would go to that church. Both of us should have handled the situation better."

"Dang, Mystic, you cut that man to the quick, didn't you?" I responded.

"Well, yeah! He did a pretty good job of cutting me too. I was acting my age. He wasn't!"

LEADERS' RESPONSIBILITY

"A lot of folks say that the young people have left the church. I believe that the church left them! When there is reality in the assembly and when the life there is vital, they will join in. The Apostle Paul places responsibility upon leaders to relate to the young and to the weak with grace and tolerance when he wrote: **'We who are strong ought to bear with the failings of the weak and not to please ourselves' (Romans 15:1 NIV).** Wisdom knows that you can't clean fish before you catch them. There needs to be an atmosphere of unconditional love that bridges the gap between the generations. Then correction can come and wisdom prevails."

OTHER MEMORIES SURFACE

Mystic began to recall other impressions from his youth.

As Mystic walked slowly by a clear gurgling stream feeding the lake in the park he loved so much, he seemed to forget for a moment where he was. He stopped, stooped down, filled his cupped hands, and drank the crystal water. He rose after drinking from the brook, looked into the distance for a few moments, and turned back towards me again.

"I remember hearing about a young boy in our church who asked his mom at bedtime what people did when they got to heaven. He knew his granddad was there and wondered how he spent his time. He hoped and even said once that he thought he was there playing golf since that was what he loved doing here, but he wasn't exactly sure.

"His mom said with great enthusiasm, 'Why Jon-Jon, we will all get to worship God for eternity.' She was sure that would fill him with delight.

"He cried, 'Oh no! If that's what you do, then I'm not sure I want to go.'

"Angus, the kind of worship he grew up with was so boring. Standing up for thirty minutes to an hour each Sunday morning singing dull songs out of a dusty hymnal meant very little to him. He could not possibly imagine how awful eternity would be if he had to sing those boring songs forever. Could you blame him?"

EACH GENERATION IS UNIQUE

"Every generation has its own musical expression. If you entirely reject the expression, you lose many within that generation. If you want to touch that generation, you must embrace its musical expression, not all of it, but much of it. If you don't, one day you will wake up and the only people in your church will be old people. When a generation's expression is rejected, whether it is skateboarding, dancing, coloring their hair, or any number of other things, the generation is in danger of being lost to the Lord.

"Many aspects of our culture are neutral. Too many church leaders live to men's opinions. Their inhibitions, fostered by public opinion and the fear of man, keep them from relating to the current generation in a receptive loving way."

Gaining *Some* Perspective, But Not Enough Yet

"As I got older my mother told me about the supernatural events that led to my birth. Now that was exciting. As she told me of the wonderful presence and power of God resident in those days, my heart burned and a sense of my own destiny rose in my heart. I could not hear enough about those extraordinary events, like Thelma Skunk's miraculous odiferous cure. You remember, Angus, how the Lord miraculously 'de-skunked' her from the smelling bad standpoint? And how Iva Benthinken was delivered from her depression and her husband Ben got saved and delivered from his smoking habit? I knew Iva after the Lord changed her. She's with the Lord now, but I remember her as the most consistently cheerful person I ever knew.

"Then my mother told me how the unusual revival ended in our church. What began in hope ended in despair that was worse in some ways than before the powerful visitation. Many who were touched by the Lord in those days became confused by the controversy and left the church. Some even lost their faith. The pressure of public opinion, especially from the religious community, became so strong that eventually the church meetings returned to a standard boring format. One fellow described their church meetings then as three hymns, an offering, and a butt kicking. The butt kicking part was his analysis of a message working folks over for what they were doing wrong."

Mystic Pauses

Deep in thought, Mystic took off his tortoise shell rimmed glasses and put one of the earpieces to his mouth. He had this contemplative far away look in his eyes for a while. Then He continued:

"That was church to me as I was growing up. By the time I was old enough to know what was going on, the supernatural aspects were long gone and almost entirely forgotten. Livingstone, Skunk Larry, and I really hated going.

"In retrospect I know that reaction to criticism over the unusual events that took place during the 'visitation by God' caused people to try to take control to ensure nothing like that would ever happen again. Nothing ever did happen again. Moving in fear always gives place to the Devil. From the descriptions of what happened during the revival, it is obvious some folks got carried away. The Holy Spirit was not responsible for every thing everyone did, but as the old timers say, 'I would rather have to put out stray sparks than live with a cold fireplace.'

"When the power of God is present, people are going to respond in many different ways, some good and some bad. All of the things that they do are not caused by the Holy Spirit but are their human reactions to the real presence of God. If you are going to allow the Spirit of God freedom to operate in your midst, then you are going to have challenges. Those are good problems, well worth having!"

CONFUSING TOO

"The church culture I lived through confused me a lot," continued Mystic. "I saw little purpose in going week after week, dressing up in Sunday clothes, clothes I didn't normally wear, and sitting in those strange benches called pews. As a child I thought, 'What a strange name for the place you sit to learn about God. *Pew!*? That's what you said when you smelled something bad!'

"I also noticed some very peculiar behavior among people. As a child I saw that some people acted one way when they were at church and an entirely different way when they weren't. I beheld the miraculous transformation of one family that I may never forget. The entire carload was screaming at each other as they rolled down the street in front of the church. Their car windows were down and I heard them arguing away, but when they turned into the parking lot and walked into the front door they were smiling and acting pleasant as could be, although the husband was sweating a lot. His red-faced wife came in right behind them smiling too.

"As a child I thought, 'Such strange powers this building has over people.'"

THE THIEF CALLED 'RELIGION'

"Mystic, you confuse me greatly. You paint a pretty bleak picture of religion. Have you not given your entire life to religion?" I quizzed him.

"No! Not the kind of religion I've been telling you about. It gets in the way of the real thing. There is a huge difference between being religious and being truly spiritual!" Mystic answered.

"I have given my entire life to Jesus Christ and His church, not to religion. I make a clear distinction between *religion* and a relationship with Jesus."

Mystic became quite animated as he explained his viewpoint. I realized how serious and passionate he was about Jesus and how upset he was that so many had been ambushed by the deceptive nature of false religion.

Mystic continued, "James, one of Jesus' brothers, identifies a type of religion that is useless. He said that **'If anyone among you thinks he is religious, and does not bridle his tongue but deceives his own heart, this one's religion is useless. Pure and undefiled religion before God and the Father is this: to visit orphans and widows in their trouble, and to keep oneself unspotted from the world'.**[20] Religion by definition means 'ceremonial observances.' James says that pure religion is helping the helpless and keeping oneself unaffected from evil attitudes and actions. But to many religion consists of 'dos and don'ts' they use to judge and criticize others. They can't live up to

---

20   James 1:26-27

their own requirements and have done much damage to young ones hungry for a true knowledge of the Lord.

"True spiritual life is expressed as a lifestyle of reality in relationship with Jesus. To know Him is life eternal. It begins when you put your trust in Him for the forgiveness of your sins and continues when you allow Him to live His life through you as your Lord. Living by a list of 'dos and don'ts' does not enable you to know Him at all. That very list energizes the 'don'ts' and disables us from doing the 'dos'.

"The Ten Commandments show us how sinful we are. They show us what is right but have no ability to enable us to live that way. We are made righteous by believing in Jesus who paid for all our failures with His death. We can only live right when we know His forgiveness and are living in relationship with Him. Until you know Him, you are fooling yourself.

"Religion that is more concerned about ceremonial observances and outward appearances than the purposes of the Lord or the people He loves is dangerous. It is a thief. It steals the very life and creativity out of the hearts of the children by resisting their unique form of creative expression in the church. So many in churches are afraid of anything new or unusual and the criticism that comes as a result of its expression. Through fear they often reject creative people forcing them into the world to express what God has given them. Being misguided through the rejection, the person, the gift, and the expression can become perverted; and many creative ones see the church, and hence the Lord, as an enemy."

GOD'S VIEWPOINT

"Angus, the Scripture emphasizes the importance of the church. God loves her and Jesus suffered the agony of a terrible death for her. I love her as well. I have seen the way the Lord loves her and what she can become. I have seen her calling, her importance. The church is the primary means God has chosen to introduce Himself to the world and release the power and grace of the kingdom of heaven."

"Why then have you said these things about the church, Mystic?" I asked.

"Because I know the untapped potential that lies there. I'm not going to ignore all that I've seen that doesn't measure up. I have seen her ultimate beauty. I want to tell the truth about what has happened to honestly touch those who have been rejected and hurt by the church world. I want to give them a way to process their hurt so they can envision her future. Anyone who catches a glimpse of this will not want to miss what God has for her. Her finest days are approaching!"

Mystic took a deep sigh and then fell silent.

"There is more I want to say about the subject of the church, but I'm too tired to finish it today," Mystic whispered. "Perhaps tomorrow…"

He did not say another word. I knew it was time to return to Magellan's house. Our drive back took about 15 minutes, 15 minutes of silence. When he left the car, we made arrangements to meet again the next day. My friend seemed so tired. As he walked back up the brick walkway to the front door, Mystic looked the oldest I remember ever seeing him. His shoulders sagged. He walked with slow shuffling steps. I could tell he carried a great burden.

CHAPTER 6

ANGUS'
LIFE
CHANGES

Angus did not sleep very well that night as he considered the events of the day listening to Mystic Moose. Their morning conversation deeply affected him in several ways. First, he could identify with Mystic's difficulties in the church world. He remembered his own struggles in church from his youth. He had long since quit going. Second, he had a deep stirring in his heart whenever Mystic spoke in such absolute terms of his real relationship with God. He was also moved deeply by the love Mystic had for the church.

Angus never realized that people could really know God. He did have some surface appreciation for the observances and ceremonies of the church. He even had a fear or perhaps a superstition about some of them. His dear Roman Catholic grandmother lived with his family for a number of years. She said her rosary every day and chastised him for not taking communion and going to confession. That didn't help much.

Back to the Park with Mystic

6:15 the next morning I picked Mystic up for our regular trip to the park. He was the proverbial early bird! I noticed something unusual about him as he walked toward my car. He possesed a real bounce in his step. *This* moose looked twenty years younger than the moose I dropped at Magellan's door the night before. He often demonstrated a resilience I had never seen in anyone else. His shoulders were erect and his antlers looked particularly broad and impressive. I bet they measured 48" from tip to tip. It was hard to even get him in the car sometimes.

Their Conversation Begins

We arrived at the park as an early morning thunderstorm broke. Thunder boomed in the distance like roaring cannons in a great ancient battle. Lightning flashed like swift swords of liquid light. The scene was a surreal canvas of nature's fury as we sat in my Mercedes SUV watching a downpour that kept us from beginning our morning walk.

Breaking the silence I said, "You look refreshed this morning."

"Well, you would be refreshed too if you went where I went last night, saw what I saw, and heard what I heard!" Mystic said.

"Where did you go?"

"Heaven!" Mystic responded matter-of-factly.

"Huh, what? Really?" (I thought, 'here we go again.' Don't people have to die before they could go to heaven? I just don't understand this moose!)

I stared at Mystic Moose with a blank *'I really just don't get this kind of thing'* look.

"Yes, I was caught up into the heavenly realm last night," Mystic replied as though he were talking about strolling down to the drugstore.

"What are you talking about, Mystic?"

"Let me just tell you what happened. Then you may understand a little more," Mystic said.

"When I went to bed last night, I was so tired and felt oppressed as well. I have learned over the years that in those circumstances the wise thing to do is counterattack, so I lay hold of some of my most powerful verses of Scripture and began to declare them aloud. One of my most effective weapons against the enemy is Psalm 91. That's what I began proclaiming early this morning about 3:00 a.m."

THE AMAZING ENCOUNTER

The day before, Mystic expended much spiritual energy rehearsing his difficult early experiences in church. It was like reliving the difficulties of his early life. He knew it was important for Angus to include his viewpoint of church in the book he was writing. Mystic was convinced that it was vital to provide understanding for the next generations. Church life is of huge importance to the ongoing plan of God. Nevertheless, the retelling of it exhausted him.

MYSTIC CONTINUED

"As I lay in bed last night feeling so wrung out and somewhat oppressed by the devil, my longtime nemesis, I began proclaiming from Psalm 91:1-4: **He who dwells in the secret place of the Most High shall abide under the shadow of the Almighty, whose power no evil foe can withstand!**

"As I spoke, I began to feel a little better, so I continued, **I will say of the Lord, He is my refuge, He is my fortress, my God, on Him will I lean and rely, and in Him will I confidently trust! Surely then He shall deliver me from the snare of the fowler and from the peril-**

ous pestilence. He shall cover me with His feathers, and under His wings I shall take refuge; His truth shall be my shield and buckler.

"Angus, the Word of God is so powerful! I have learned from personal experiences that its strength is released when believed and spoken! As I proclaimed these vital verses I felt more confident. The Lord's strength seeped into my very soul. So I did it again, this time with renewed strength and more conviction.

"He who dwells in the secret place of the Most High shall abide under the shadow of the Almighty, whose power no evil foe can withstand! I will say of the Lord, He is my refuge, He is my fortress, my God, on Him will I lean and rely, and in Him will I confidently trust! Surely then He shall deliver me from the snare of the fowler and from the perilous pestilence. He shall cover me with His feathers, and under His wings I shall take refuge; His truth shall be my shield and buckler.

"Suddenly, I saw what looked to be an air shaft suspended above my head that went right through the ceiling. I didn't see it appear. It was as if it had always been there but I never noticed it. I knew instinctively that I could climb in and it would carry me into the realm of the heavens. So I did just that. I leaped up into it. I shot through the air at a blinding rate. As I zoomed through the atmospheric realm of the evil one, (he is known as the prince of the power of the air), I heard demonic voices saying, 'Hey, you can't come through here!' I began laughing because I knew their attempts to stop me were in vain. I was going and that was all there was to it!

"I landed in the heavens under a huge dark wing. It must have been at least 8'0" tall. Precious and semi-precious stones of all descriptions, the size of tennis balls and larger, were not just attached to it but exuded from it. I have never seen anything like it in my life. Gold and silver particles and other precious metals were coming out of the wing. I was confused. I thought angel's wings would be white! I didn't understand why the place was not bright. Then I realized something. Had I not just boldly said that I would dwell in the *secret place* of the Most High and abide *under the shadow* of the Almighty? Had I not just declared that He would deliver me from the snare of the fowler, you know, the bird catcher? Had I not emphatically proclaimed: **He shall cover me with His feathers, and under His wings I shall take refuge?** I was not under a massive angel's wing. I had taken refuge in the heavenly realm under the wing of the Great Eagle, the One of whom I had proclaimed."

ANGUS OBJECTS

"Whoa, whoa, whoa, wait a minute!" said Angus. "Timeout… time…out!"

At that point Angus actually made the timeout signal college basketball coaches use to stop play.

"Do you really expect me to believe this crazy stuff!? Airshafts, tennis ball size rubies, huge brown wings, demons in midair talking to you? C'mon Mystic, that's way outside of ridiculous!"

Mystic responded, "I don't believe in pressuring people, especially in the areas of beliefs or conscience. Angus, I certainly won't try to force you either. I can only tell you what happened. I know it's a huge stretch for you, but what about the parting of the Red Sea, the drowning of the Egyptian army, the miraculous rescue of the two million Jewish slaves? That happened too, according to the Bible. Then there's Noah's ark, Elijah who was swept up to heaven in a whirlwind, Jesus walking on the water, and the conference Jesus had on the Mount of Transfiguration with Moses, who died many years earlier, and Elijah who never died! All of that plus much more is in the Bible that many people believe."

"I just don't know," sputtered Angus McAlpine. "I just don't know! How do you expect me to believe this stuff, never mind write this stuff?"

Mystic Continued

"Angus, the book you are writing is not about you! It's not about me either really but about what God can do in a life. These things are integral parts of my life, and they are true. So many people are afraid of the supernatural. That fear permeates so much of Christianity, but it's a deception. Many rejecters believe in supernatural evil but deny the kinds of things that I told you about, all of which have greatly encouraged me. The encounters made me love God more, not less. Fear of the supernatural has got to end. I once attended a private gathering of Christian millionaire and billionaire businessmen. One of them testified that God gave him his most successful business ideas in dreams. Then he quickly countered, 'And if you ever repeat what I just said, I'll deny that it's true or that I ever said it!'

"When believers are intimidated into concealing their valuable faith experiences, then great spiritual encouragement and substance are lost. Think of Isaiah's great prophetic plea about the wonders he saw of the redemption of Jesus hundreds of years before it occurred; **'Who has believed our report? And to whom has the arm of the Lord been revealed?'**[21] If people are silent about the marvelous things like these that they know are true, Angus, how will others have an opportunity to consider the wonderful, creative mysteries of our great God? Paul spoke of 'the hidden riches of wisdom and knowledge' that are in Christ and the 'unsearchable riches of Christ' as part of the great mystery of God. He also wrote, **'But the natural man does not receive the things of the Spirit of God, for they are foolishness to him; nor can he know them, because they are spiritually discerned.'**[22] None of the things I told you will lead one away from God. They do the opposite for me. They make me hungry to know this awesome, creative, inventive God more and more. They are not dangerous, but if you let

---

21   Isaiah 53:1

22   1 Corinthians 2:14

me continue you will see just how encouraging they are.

"King Solomon said, **'It is the glory of God to conceal a matter, but the glory of kings is to search out a matter.'**[23] I am an energetic pursuer of the great realities of my God. Alas, dear Angus. Please humor this old saintly moose a little more and let me continue, for I have yet to get to the real significance of this encounter."

"Oh my," Angus moaned. "There's more?"

"Much more. The Lord showed me that the available resources of heaven are much greater than we ever considered. He authorized me to bring them back and distribute them!"

"And that works how, Mystic?" Angus hardly disguised his sarcasm.

Angus was obviously struggling but Mystic knew that deep down under all his reticence and unbelief, he really wanted to know more.

"By faith, Angus," Mystic said a little impatiently. "Everything works by faith, but let me continue. I'm on a roll here.

"The Lord authorized me to bring back and release what He described as five distinct wagons of divine substance. In the encounter, I knew that I could find further significance and understanding of them in the Biblical story of Joseph's restoration with his father Jacob and his brothers. One of the characteristics of these experiences, Angus, is that you just know things instinctively and automatically."

WAGON #1

"The first wagon was called *Deliverance from Deserved Consequences.* Jesus loves people so much that He wants to set them free from their bad choices and decisions. He was saying, 'You did the wrong thing. You made the wrong choice. Yes, you sinned but I want to set you free from what you deserve.'"

---

23   Proverbs 25:2

Angus Catches a Glimpse

"My goodness," Angus exclaimed. "You mean He wants to help people who don't deserve it?" Like a sudden flash of lightning, Angus caught a brief glimpse of the heart of God.

"Ah, yes. No one deserves God's help. See how important these supernatural encounters really are? They have the power to suddenly illuminate and help people enjoy all the blessings of the gospel in a fresh way, but let me continue."

Wagon #2

"The second one was a wagon called *Deliverance from Criticism and the Critical Spirit!* Jesus knows the destructive power of critical words people have spoken. He wants to set wounded people free to be whom *He* says they are.

"That wagon also provides deliverance from being critical. Many people shoot themselves in the foot. Jesus warned that we would be judged and condemned in direct proportion to our judgment and condemnation of others. Many have reaped condemnation from their own words, ones they sowed through criticizing others."

Wagon #3

"The third wagon was a wagon called *Provision*. God wants to provide for the needs and desires of His people. Angus, there is no shortage in heaven of anything that we may need in earth. When Jesus taught us to pray, 'Your Kingdom come in earth as it is in heaven,'[24] He meant that what happens in heaven can be accessed by us down here. There are no poor people in heaven, no sick, no depressed either! Do you think God will answer whatever prayer Jesus told us to pray? I know He will!"

---

24   Matthew 6:10

HEAVEN'S ECONOMY

"I have a good friend named Clever Gleeson, an interesting man of Canadian descent. He once piloted planes in western Canada that put out those huge seasonal forest fires. He was also a missionary to the Inuit people in Alaska and lover of whale blubber. I always enjoyed him. He didn't have a hair on his head and looked a lot like Mister Clean, the character you see in the cleansing product ads. Quite a character!"

CLEVER'S TESTIMONY

"He once told me, 'Mystic, one December evening I meditated on God's goodness. After doing so about twenty minutes I had a vision as vivid as any movie. The Spirit of the Lord showed me things in heaven that shocked me.'

"'I saw huge cylindrical storage tanks, many rows of them. I asked the Lord what these tanks were for. He said, "fuel for the elect." It was gasoline for vehicles owned by believers. It was a supernatural supply that could be accessed by faith. The Lord then held up one of your American $1.00 bills and told me, "The dollar enables people access to this world's supply, but faith in Me will give you access to Heaven's supply." Mystic, there is an economy in Heaven that is much stronger and more stable than the economy of the world. It is an economy that cannot be shaken.'

"'Mystic, some things in the vision confused me at first,' Clever continued. 'I also saw parking lots full of brand new cars. Some dated back to the 1950's and 1930's. This is what confused me. At first I thought they must be restored antique cars. The Lord seemed to hear my thoughts. He instantly responded as I stood there looking at them: "They are not rebuilt automobiles, Clever. They are brand new models from decades ago. No one ever accessed the faith for them, so they are still here."'"

"'Mystic *that* really blew my mind. I also had the sense that there is provision in heaven for technology that does not exist yet, waiting there for a future generation.'

"You see Angus, our relationship with heaven and what is available there is not the way we *think* it is but the way it *actually* is. We don't control heavenly reality by our belief system. We only control our ability to obtain it by our faith and insight."

WAGON #4

"The fourth was a wagon called *Hope*. Hope is one thing we cannot do without. It is the foundation for faith, for **'faith is the substance of things hoped for, the evidence of things not seen."**[25] The Apostle Paul said that hope anchors our soul, Angus. That means true spiritual hope secures our entire mental welfare and energizes our life of faith! One who truly knows Jesus is filled with a hope that cannot be extinguished!

"Angus, to convince me of the importance of this wagon called *Hope,* the Lord gave me another encounter. Early in the morning as I awakened, a man named Charles Hope appeared to me in my bedroom. I'm not saying he was really there. It may have been a dream or vision. It is difficult to explain the nature of some of these experiences. I stared right into his smiling face. He said, 'Hello. I'm going to be your new best friend.' He wore a sweater and hat, both with the National Football League emblems on them for the Philadelphia Eagles. He was standing on a newly paved road that went right by my bed. Then the Lord said this about him. 'He is a rogue.' That sounded quite strange to me, but as I investigated the definition of the word, I understood that it is someone that cannot be controlled, Angus. That is exactly what the world needs, a living hope that cannot be controlled!"

---

25   Hebrews 11:1

"That's so wild, Mystic. Why would the man have NFL emblems on his sweater and hat? What does football have to do with hope?"

PICTURES, ONE OF GOD'S LANGUAGES

"Angus, have you heard of the expression, 'A picture is worth a thousand words'?"

"Uh, yes, sure. My mother used to say that."

"Think about it, Angus. Jesus spoke in word pictures as one of His primary means of communicating spiritual truths. For example, He said, **'the kingdom of heaven is like treasure hidden in a field, which a man found and hid; and for joy over it he goes and sells all that he has and buys that field'.**[26] He could have told the disciples that the kingdom is valuable.

"Or, **'A good man out of the treasure of his heart brings forth good things, and an evil man out of the evil treasure brings forth evil things.'**[27] Instead, He might have just said that good men speak honest things.

"His parable describing the Pharisees is quite poignant. **'Every plant which My heavenly Father has not planted will be uprooted. Let them alone. They are blind leaders of the blind. And if the blind leads the blind, both will fall into the ditch.'**[28] Jesus could have said that the Pharisees were in danger of losing their place of authority and that they should be ignored. Instead, He used word pictures so men could remember the ideas and gain insight about the spiritual dimension for normal everyday things around them. His word pictures had the capacity to indelibly imprint each message on their minds."

---

26   Matthew 13:44
27   Matthew 12:35
28   Matthew 15:13-14

Back to Charles Hope

"Well, then what did it mean to you, you know, the man named *Hope* and the Philadelphia Eagle stuff? It doesn't mean anything to me," Angus responded.

"Great question, Angus. Interpreting spiritual encounters is more of an art form than an exact science, just as word pictures contain more creative content than lifeless principles. The encounter's primary purpose is to encourage, build up, and inspire people. The primary meaning is that I have a 'living Hope' that cannot be controlled. *It* is actually a *He*, the resurrected Jesus Christ. 'Being my new best friend' speaks of His love, constant availability, and desire to be close to me. *Charles* means 'free man.' This *Hope* is free! He cannot be bound and cannot be bought or earned. Being my *new* best friend reveals that He exists in a perpetual newness of life, that death and decay have no more power over Him."

"Interesting analysis, Mystic," Angus said. "What about the Philadelphia Eagles part?"

Mystic's Interpretation Unfolds

"Jesus gave prophetic messages for seven different churches to John the Apostle while he was exiled on the Isle of Patmos. The church at Philadelphia was one of two to receive commendations instead of rebukes. Philadelphia means 'brotherly love' or 'love of the brethren.' The Philadelphia emblem speaks of how hope thrives in a community atmosphere where brotherly love is constant. The eagle describes believers who use the winds of adversity to soar over their circumstances. Most birds flap to stay airborne. Eagles mount up on the winds and soar for hours with little effort.

"The Philadelphia Eagles NFL football team has developed a reputation for giving players a second chance. They have signed some players who failed miserably only to see them excel in an atmosphere of acceptance and redemption. You see, hope flourishes in a redemptive community.

"Angus, the fact that Charles Hope wore a hat and a sweater bearing the Philadelphia Eagles' emblem reveals that love based hope will protect your mind and heart. It will warm you when the chill of indifference or opposition comes your way. Hope secures our entire mental state, enabling us to believe God for the fulfillment of His promises and to have a sound mind at all times. The future belongs to those who have the most hope. Can you see now how invaluable these encounters are?"

"Still, Mystic, all of this is so foreign to me. I am really at a loss for words."

WAGON # 5

Mystic reminded Angus that there was another wagon.

"Angus, wagon number five has great significance. It was called, *A New Vision for the United States*. I knew instinctively during this encounter that I could understand the significance of the wagons more clearly through the Bible story of Joseph and the amazing restoration of his family. Genesis 37 begins the story."

YOUNG JOSEPH

"Joseph, Jacob's youngest and favorite of eleven sons, provoked his brothers to great jealousy. They didn't get along at all. Jacob dressed Joseph in a coat of many colors, a visible and constant token of his favoritism, and his brothers hated him for it.

"At seventeen years of age, Joseph had two amazingly accurate dreams that indicated he would be the most prominent of all the sons of Jacob. He infuriated his brothers when he told them of these dreams. The only problem, Angus, is that they came to pass many years later.

"One day while Joseph's brothers fed their father's flocks in a distant location Jacob sent Joseph to see how they fared. When his brothers saw him coming in the distance, they conspired to kill him. One brother said sarcastically, 'Behold, the master of dreams is coming!' When he arrived they stripped him of his colorful clothes, threw him in a deep pit, and sat down to eat.

"Angus, these guys were high-level scoundrels. Suddenly, upon the horizon appeared a caravan of Ishmaelite traders. Joseph's shrewd brothers made an instant business decision and sold him as a slave rather than kill him. Before returning home, the brothers killed an animal and dipped Joseph's clothes in its blood. They presented the bloody tunic to their father Jacob who concluded that wild animals killed his beloved Joseph. The loss of his favorite son devastated Jacob."

JOSEPH EMERGES

"My friend, God watched over Joseph in an amazing way. The Ishmaelite traders took him to Egypt and sold him as a slave. Through a series of remarkable events over many years, Pharaoh appointed him the second most powerful man in all Egypt. A great famine overtook the world; but because of Joseph's wise administration, Egypt was prepared. The Lord showed Joseph the coming years of famine through divine interpretation of Pharaoh's dreams and directed him to store huge deposits of food. As the seven-year famine progressed, surrounding nations flooded to Egypt and appeared before Joseph to procure food to survive. Jacob sent his sons to get some too.

"When the sons of Jacob arrived in Egypt and bowed down to Joseph, he recognized them but they did not know it was him. He had been gone twenty-two years! Through several heartrending episodes, Joseph revealed himself to them and provided for their welfare. When he learned that his father was alive, he sent wagons loaded with heaps of provisions, the best Egypt had to offer."

MYSTIC READS TO ANGUS

"Oh my, Angus. This story is so amazing."

Mystic reached up and took his Bible off the dashboard where it sat during their ride over to the park. He rarely went anywhere without it.

"Although Joseph provided some food for his family, Jacob did not yet know that Joseph was live. Let me read some of this incredible story to you from Genesis 45."

In his deep, rich, gravelly voice, Mystic read:

> **"And Joseph sent to his father these things: ten donkeys loaded with the good things of Egypt, and ten female donkeys loaded with grain, bread, and food for his father and for the journey…"**

> **"Then they went up out of Egypt, and came to the land of Canaan to Jacob their father. And they told him, saying, 'Joseph is still alive, and he is governor over all the land of Egypt.' And Jacob's heart stood still, because he did not believe them."**[29]

Mystic continued:

> **"But when they told him all the words which Joseph had said to them, and when he saw the _wagons_ which Joseph had sent to carry him, the spirit of Jacob their father revived."**[30]

"Angus. Did you see that? Jacob could not believe his son was still alive until he saw the wagons, and then he revived! The hope filled

---

29   Genesis 45:23 & 26
30   Genesis 45:27 KJV

message of the five wagons the Lord showed me has the capacity to revive people!"

Mystic Gets Excited

Then Mystic spoke as exuberantly as Angus had ever heard him.

"Our hearts will revive when we see the amazing resources of heaven that Christ Jesus provided for the world! This is the message of the wagons: Freedom for those who have been criticized, hope for the hopeless, deliverance for the guilty, and provision for every needy soul! And a new vision for our great nation!"

New Vision for Our Nation

"Angus, Joseph brought his entire family to Egypt to preserve their lives and heritage. This is a perfect picture of the mercy of God. Joseph's brothers acted so wickedly in their treatment of him, yet he wanted to care for them anyway.

"Remember the wagon called *New Vision for the United States?*"

"Yes, Mystic, but how does that work? I never heard that the United States is mentioned in the Bible," Angus responded.

"I know, I know," Mystic said. "The Bible never says the words 'United States', but there is a promise hidden in the story that can really encourage our nation, or any nation on the face of the earth for that matter! According to the story, Pharaoh provided a certain area of his nation for Jacob's family called Goshen. It was the very best place in all Egypt. The name Goshen literally means 'drawing near.'

"The Lord wants to provide such a place for our nation. James, the Lord's natural brother and one of the major leaders of the early church wrote: **'Draw near to God and He will draw near to you.'**[31] If our nation will draw near to God, He will draw near to us and change

---

31 James 4:8

our nation! I believe that is going to happen in the United States. We are on the verge of another Great Spiritual Awakening that shall once again reshape our nation.

"Just as the wagons brought the family of Jacob to Goshen, the enablement of heaven can bring our nation to another great place!"

"Let me ask you a question, Mystic. How in the world would your vision ever really affect anyone? It still makes very little sense to me. What difference does it make that you saw a bunch of wagons in some kind of weird experience?"

Significance of the Wagons

"Another great question, Angus. We find the answer in the basic construction of the wagons. Wagons are pulled by a part termed 'the tongue.' The wagons I saw were ancient wooden ones with wheels having wooden spokes. Years ago, buckets made out of oak were called *oaken* buckets. In that same sense the wagon wheels could be called *spoken* wheels. The contents of these five wagons can be obtained by exercising faith through the 'spoken' word. This same message comes from the book of Proverbs: **'Death and life are in the power of the tongue, and those who love it will eat its fruit.'**[32]

"Angus, anyone can access the content of these wagons by believing and speaking their reality. Paul described this basic process of obtaining spiritual benefit when he wrote, **'For with the heart man believes unto righteousness and with the mouth confession is made unto salvation.'**[33]

"Those wagons were so full that I heard the substance in them fall from the heavens and hit the floor on the earth where I had the encounter. Jesus has so much that He wants us to have. He is so wonderful. The story of Joseph and the restoration of his family is filled

---

32   Proverbs 18:21

33   Romans 10:10

with hope and insight. Jacob and his family thought for years that Joseph was dead. He was not only alive, but he was Lord of all Egypt. This is such a great picture of our Lord Jesus. He was the one who was dead but ever lives to come to our aid. He is Lord of all and wants to do so much more for us than Joseph ever did for his family!"

THE STORM ENDS

The storm subsided as Mystic finished explaining the significance of the five wagons encounter. The sun appeared again through the clouds and lighted the forest lake. Birds began chirping. A warm breeze rustled the great oaks and exacted its toll of fragrant pine scent from the evergreens. It looked like a scene from paradise.

"My, the storm has ended. Let's get out and walk, Angus," Mystic suggested. "I want to finish what I began yesterday. I have more to tell you about my experiences in church as a child."

Mystic and Angus began walking. They rounded the curve in the muddy trail that pierced through the forest and emerged at the lake's shore.

"I felt like I left you a little cold and confused yesterday, Angus."

"Sort of. Maybe…" Angus' voice trailed off.

TWO DIFFERENT PLANETS

Angus wasn't sure what he thought about his dialogues with this unusual moose. Mystic's entire life was so foreign to him.

"Mystic, it's as though we come from two different planets, you and I."

"Not really," Mystic replied. "We may be more alike than you realize."

Mystic hesitated and with great compassion asked, "Angus, how do you like *your* planet?"

"Not very well. Not now, especially since Marilyn died," Angus said.

"The Lord is going to do something about that for you, Angus. Just give Him some more time and your joy shall return. The psalmist accurately described you when he said, **'Weeping may endure for a night but joy comes in the morning'**.[34] I see your life making a big turn."

Angus drew quiet. He didn't want to continue talking with Mystic about his own situation. It was too painful. The only way he knew to deal with his inner turmoil was to ignore it.

ANGUS CHANGES THE SUBJECT

"What else did you want to tell me about your early life, Mystic?" Angus said, changing the uncomfortable subject.

"There were several things that happened on a regular basis at church that confused me as a child. I remember my first experience with the Lord's Supper. When I heard one Sunday that we were going to have the Lord's Supper, I got quite excited. I thought maybe I would finally get to see the Lord and could only imagine what we were going to eat at the supper that was for Him. I had two problems: first, I never got any supper and second, I watched the people very closely who did, and it was hardly enough to eat."

SKUNK LARRY'S VIEW

"On our way home from church that day, Skunk Larry and I discussed the proceedings. His explanation of how disappointed he was mirrored my sentiments exactly. He said to me, 'Teddy, I think it should be called the Lord's snack. All I saw was small crackers and tiny cups of grape juice. It would have been enough for some of our smaller brethren, like the mice, but not for us! And we didn't even get

---

34   Psalm 30:5

any.' Neither of us understood why you would have a supper called the Lord's Supper when He was not there."

ANGUS IS OFFENDED

"Mystic, that sounds plain sacrilegious to me," Angus said with a nervous hesitancy in his voice.

"I find it interesting that you have an opinion about what you believe to be sacrilegious, Angus, especially since by your own admission you have lived a decidedly non-religious life. I like that though. Yes, I like that a lot," Mystic said with real sincerity, "for exactly three reasons. It proves to me your conscience is still alive, you continue to have spiritual desires, and you aren't afraid to disagree with me and ask honest yet uncomfortable questions. That makes my point. Honest responses to things not understood are not sacrilegious. Church mystified me when I was a child. How many other children have been just as confused by the way we have done church?

"The church should be the place where both young and old can *honestly* inquire into the mysteries of God without being chastised or criticized. My youthful inquisitiveness was but a natural desire to know and understand the things of God. How often have honest heartfelt questions been squelched? God is the God of truth, and He welcomes truthful inquiry and authentic responses."

HONESTY VALUED

"I love it about Jesus that He was never intimidated or offended by truly honest people. The young Apostle John, one of His very best friends, describes a meeting Jesus had with a young man named Nathanael.[35] Nathanael's friend Philip met Jesus first and believed He was the Messiah whom God promised for centuries through His prophets and written records.

---

35   John 1:43-51

"Philip told Nathanael, 'We've found the One Moses wrote of in the Law, the One preached by the prophets. It's Jesus, Joseph's son, the one from Nazareth!'

"Nathanael responded to Philip's excited revelation, 'He's from Nazareth!? You have got to be kidding. Can any thing good possibly come from that sorry place?'

"'Come see for yourself, Nathanael,' Philip challenged. So Nathanael went with Philip to check out this Jesus.

"Upon seeing Nathanael, Jesus exclaimed, 'Aha! Standing before Me is an Israelite who has not one false bone in his body!'"

Nathanael Shocked

"Nathanael probably scratched his head. 'Where did you get that idea? You don't know me,' he responded.

"Jesus said, 'Before, when Philip called you, when you were under the fig tree. I was watching!'

"Nathanael said to Jesus, 'Rabbi, You are the Son of God, the King of Israel!'"

Mystic Explains

"Angus, Jesus supernaturally heard what Nathanael said to Philip about Him under the fig tree. He was not offended by it. He liked it! Nathanael was so affected by the power of Jesus' amazing insight and gracious response that he instantly believed Him to be the One for whom Israel had been waiting.

"Our Father welcomes seekers of truth no matter what the age. Jesus told us that His Father seeks those who will worship Him in spirit and truth.[36] The Pharisees and sometimes even His own disciples

---

36   John 4:23-24

overlooked the people Jesus was looking for, the young, the children, the tax collectors, the prostitutes, and you, Angus!

"The disciples saw children as nuisances. Jesus saw them as significant, ones to learn from, ones to love. He told them, 'Permit the little children to come unto Me, and forbid them not: for of such is the kingdom of God.'[37] He said it was better if a man had never lived than to offend one of the little ones He loved. **'It would be better for him if a millstone were hung around his neck, and he were thrown into the sea, than that he should offend one of these little ones.'**[38]

"Jesus was accused of associating with all manner of unsavory folks. He came to look for and help all who were lost. He put a high premium on folks just like Nathanael, those who were honest.

"The Psalmist declared:

> **"The LORD is near to all who call upon Him,**
> **to all who call upon Him in truth. He will fulfill**
> **the desire of those who fear Him; He also will hear**
> **their cry and save them."**[39]

"Angus, God is near every one who calls upon Him in truthfulness. The point is not just that He is near everyone, since we know that God is everywhere at all times. How many people find Him and are truly helped by Him? The point is that He is inclined toward everyone who calls upon Him in gut level honesty."

BART FRIDAY GETS MARRIED

"I had a neighborhood friend named Bart Friday. We went to school together for years. He was Lamar Skunk's best friend. You remember Lamar? He's the one who stole my G.I. Joe at the sand

---

37 Mark 10:14
38 Luke 17:2
39 Psalm 145:18-19

8

pile when I was a kid. Well, Bart was a very devout young man. After college his two basic goals were to get married and become a pastor. He wanted to be married in the worst way. He had a girlfriend named Joanie McNinch. She was something special. They had a pretty rocky relationship for about a year. They broke up four or five times, mostly because Bart was so unsure of himself. Some problematic female relationships in high school and college messed him up pretty well. He also wanted to be sure to marry the girl the Lord had for him.

"The last time they got back together Joanie told him if he broke up with her one more time, she would be done with him. So he got confused again and broke up with her another time. Joanie was heartbroken. The relationship was over, and both stayed messed up the better part of a year afterwards.

"Bart and the young McNinch girl attended the same small church. Neither of them left. Nobody was happy with the way he treated her. Some warned her that Bart was just bad news. The situation proved to be extremely embarrassing and painful for both of them.

"Bart told me that was one of the most miserable times of his life. Angus, then he told me this incredible story of how he and Joanie got back together and got married."

Bart Tells His Story

"Mystic, I was *so* troubled those months after I broke Joanie's heart not just once, but again and again. I had not felt the Lord's presence for a good long while. I remember it like it was yesterday. One day I left on lunch break from my job at the Restaurant Equipment Supply store where I worked. I often went to a nearby Christian bookstore, probably looking for answers for how I had gotten myself so messed up. Suddenly, as I drove over, the sweet, peaceful, marvelous presence of the Lord literally came into the car. I thought, 'Oh, my...where have You been Lord?'

"Then, in the quietness of my heart, the Lord asked me, 'Bart, do you want to get married?'

"I couldn't help but think, 'What!? Lord, of course I do. That's what I've wanted this whole time.'

"Actually, Mystic," Bart told me, "I couldn't believe the Lord asked me that question. He knew well what I was going through with Joanie.

"Then the Lord asked me another question – 'Bart, what kind of girl would you like to marry?'

"I said, 'Well, you know, the kind of girl that would be good to help me in the ministry. It would be great if she could maybe play the piano, help with kids ministry, things like that!'"

THE LORD EXITS

"Faster than His presence entered my car, He abruptly left. I felt the same depressed way as I had for months before His sudden presence surprised to me in the car that day. I thought, 'I sure must have given the Lord the wrong answer.' As soon as I came to that conclusion, His presence flooded right back into the car again.

"The Lord spoke, 'Come on Bart, what kind of woman do you really want?'"

BART ANSWERS HONESTLY

"'Oh, that?!' I said, sort of shocked. I knew the Lord was asking me to be gut level honest. The kind of girl I wanted had nothing to do with pianos, Sunday school teaching, or anything remotely connected. I wanted to marry a girl who looked like the standard centerfold model of every carnal boy's dreams. I gave the Lord the basic description of the kind of girl I had always wanted, size, shape, physical description and all.

"The Lord said, 'Alright. That's more like it. I knew it all along.'

Mystic, then He left. And I was no longer troubled but hopeful that He was on the scene ready to work on my behalf. I was also thoroughly confused. How could I admit to what I really wanted and not be in trouble for it? It was lustful."

"So what happened then, Bart?" I asked. "Mystic, I went to see Joanie and asked her to marry me. She said yes. We were married that fall and have been happy ever since! The things I wanted were not necessarily right or even noble. Some of them were plain lustful, but I learned that day that the Lord is '**Near to all them that call upon Him . . . that call upon Him** *in truth.*[40] He highly values honesty! He meets us where we are, no matter where that is. The trick is to be honest about where you are no matter how bad it is!"

ANGUS LISTENED INTENTLY

Mystic saw Angus listening closely and so continued, "You may remember the story of Jesus meeting a Samaritan woman at Jacob's well. As a rule the Jews and the Samaritans did not so much as speak with one another. Normally Jews despised Samaritans as an impure race, a nation of idolaters who perverted true Judaism. Nor did men and women converse with one another freely in public in the culture of the day. Nevertheless, Jesus immediately asked the woman to give Him water from the well. When she hesitated, He told her that He could give her a kind of living water that would enable her to never thirst again. That water would become in her a fountain that would spring up into everlasting life."

ANGUS IS THIRSTY

Angus, not knowing the Bible very well, had never heard this story. As he listened to the promise Jesus made, he too wondered if such water existed and how to get it if it did. He had a deep thirst that

---

40   Psalm 145:18

had not been quenched. Losing Marilyn only intensified his feelings of desperation.

Angus said, "What happened then? What did Jesus say to her? How could He give her such a thing?" Mystic's description of the woman's encounter with Jesus was so real to him that Angus could not hold back his questions. He thought it strange that Mystic told this story as though he knew Jesus personally.

"She said to Jesus, 'Give me this water so that I won't be thirsty again and have to keep coming down here to this well.'"

"Did He do it? Did Jesus give her His mysterious water?" questioned Angus.

"He asked her to do something that did not make any sense to her. He asked her to go get her husband," Mystic answered.

"That doesn't make any sense. What did going to get her husband have to do with drinking the living water?"

Mystic sat quietly, allowing R. Angus McAlpine to linger in his own questioning. He knew that the Lord wanted to help him just as He helped the woman at the well so many years ago. Mystic sensed the Lord drawing Angus closer to Himself. This conversation was one more link in the Lord's process of reaching into Angus' heart to change and help him.

MYSTIC BREAKS THE SILENCE

"The woman said to Jesus, 'I have no husband.' Angus, what she told Him was true, but not *the* truth."

"That doesn't make sense, either," countered Angus.

"Jesus responded to the woman, 'You have well said, "I have no husband," for you have had five husbands and the one whom you now have is not your husband; in that you spoke truly.'

"It is true that she did not have a husband, but the truth is she was living with a man to whom she was not married and had five husbands before him. Jesus had a word of knowledge, a kind of supernatural insight about this woman's personal affairs that brought her to a place of facing the truth about herself."

"But what does that have to do with living water?"

"Everything, Angus. Jesus was offering her unlimited inner life and satisfaction if she would acknowledge the sin in her life and her own need. Her honesty unleashed the provision for the deep needs that she tried to satisfy through her immorality.

"When she was honest, she began to drink from that fountain of life. She was so touched by the power of her conversation with Jesus that she left her water pot and went back to the city to tell everyone about the Man she met who told her 'all things ever she did'[41] and what He had done for her. First of all, she could hardly believe that He would even talk to her. She was utterly amazed by the word of knowledge He had about her relationships. Then she could not overcome His acceptance of her, in light of her immorality. His acceptance set her free from the cause of her sinfulness. She never knew true approval from any man until she met Jesus at Jacob's well. Yes, there is a well for Jacob, the prototypical natural man in need of God. Jesus has a well for all the *Jacobs* struggling through life in need of healing and deliverance in the midst of their difficulties."

ANGUS'S BREAKTHROUGH

Light dawned in Angus' heart. "That's amazing," Angus said. "As the woman admitted her *real* thirst, Jesus provided the real water!"

"Yes, Angus, you have said it even better than I have. When the woman admitted her real thirst, Jesus provided the real water. That

---

41   John 4:29

is the transforming power of meeting Jesus in truth. By the way, that is exactly what church should be like, a place where people have an amazing and utterly real experience with God.

"Angus, one could say of that woman that she was the wrong race, a despised gender, had bad theology, asked Jesus the wrong questions, gave Him the wrong answers, had the wrong morality; but when she was honest with Jesus, she entered into a brand new life. She left that well without her water pot. She was no longer thirsty! She returned home and began telling everyone about the wonderful man she had met!"

Great tears welled up in Angus McAlpine's eyes. Soon they streamed down his cheeks into his beard and dropped down on his alpaca sweater.

"I want to meet Jesus the way that woman did, Mystic, and I want to know Him as well as you do. But I don't know how to do it...."

His voice trailed off as his eyes moved from Mystic's to the ground. Angus began to sob as he fell into Mystic's chest. Years of frustration from the life he lived and his heartache from Marilyn's death began to pour out of his soul. A deep cry of anguish racked his body as Mystic engulfed him and began to pray.

"Father, in the name of Christ Jesus, I bind every tormentor and release the enemy from any assignment he has against this my friend."

Angus sighed deeply, almost fainting. Mystic steadied him, holding him by the shoulders as he regained his balance. He looked up at Mystic and gazed deeply into his eyes. As Mystic looked back he saw in Angus' eyes a clarity that was not there before.

Mystic thought to himself, "Just as the Lord showed me in last night's dream...."

With a broad smile and twinkling eyes Moose spoke to Angus with authority, "Turn to Jesus from your former life. Forsake your sins, receive Him and submit to Him as your Lord."

And that is exactly what R. Angus McAlpine did.

"Jesus," Angus boldly called, "give me this water! I want to know You like Mystic does."

Angus called out for Jesus to save him. There standing beside the crystal clear stream that fed the lake in the forest where the two of them walked so many times, Angus McAlpine was born from above. Before Mystic's very eyes, R. Angus became a brand new person.

Suddenly, Angus heaved with a great shudder and coughed violently. When he stopped and calmed down he said, "What in the world just happened to me? It's as if something deep inside just left!"

"I'll explain it later, Angus. But you need to be baptized in water. Why not do it right now?"

Angus was startled at the idea but quickly determined to go the distance with the Lord. He held back far too long.

"Why not?" Angus exclaimed, and in his excitement he rushed into the clear lake with all of his clothes on. Then he realized Mystic Moose needed help getting in, and he returned to give him a hand as they waded back into the cool water. They steadied themselves beside a flat-bottomed aluminum johnboat tied to the nearby dock.

Just like multitudes have done down through the ages, Mystic baptized Angus in water. As he came up out of the watery grave, he shouted in exhilaration. Then he began to speak in a new language as the Holy Spirit enabled him. Mystic was taken by surprise because of the suddenness of the unique language Angus spoke since he had forgotten to tell Angus that this could happen to him.

THE RAINBOW TROUT PROMISE

Suddenly, as the sun broke out from behind the clouds, a rainbow trout leapt out of the water and landed in the boat beside them.

Mystic looked at the trout flopping around in the boat as the dancing sunlight highlighted all its colors and then looked at Angus.

"Angus, centuries ago the Lord gave us the rainbow in the sky as a sign of assurance that the dark days of the flood would never return to cover the earth. Today He has given you this rainbow trout as a sign that the dark days of depression that dogged your life since the death of your wife shall never return."

SUDDEN OUTPOURING OF JOY

Mystic's abrupt proclamation so shocked and startled Angus that he immediately burst into laughter. The depression was broken and the two of them began to laugh uproariously together. They became so intoxicated with the presence of God that they could hardly walk back to the shore. They began flailing and flopping around in the water like two inebriated manatees.

Mystic began to praise and thank God with all his heart. The Lord brought a rush of refreshing and joy into Angus' heart as well. He never felt so clean in all His life. Now a peace he never knew before flooded his heart. It took them fifteen minutes to climb out of the waters of joy where Angus was baptized.

TWO SOGGY BROTHERS

As the two soggy brothers began to slosh their way back to Angus' car, Mystic thought, "Later I must continue telling Angus my testimony of how I overcame other hurdles to enter the ministry. Now is a time to enjoy the Lord and praise Him for what He has done in his life."

"Angus, how does it feel to be a brand new man? Welcome into the family of God. You, my good man, have been translated out of the kingdom of darkness into the Kingdom of the Son of His love!"

Jesus Christ had so touched Angus that he told three people about it between the park and Magellan Matthews' home. On the way out of the park, Angus spotted the Park Ranger. The Ranger recognized Angus and Mystic from their regular trips to the park.

Angus' exuberance knew no bounds. As he and Mystic, still wet from the spontaneous baptism, walked toward the Ranger, Angus joyfully blurted, "I met Jesus a few minutes ago by the lake and He gave me living water. I am not near as thirsty as I had been for many years!"

Angus had no idea how little sense he was making but continued to gush right along with his newfound joy. "I have never felt so wonderful in all my life. You must ask Jesus for a drink of this water yourself. Do you want some?"

THE RANGER SCRATCHES HIS HEAD

The Park Ranger had been watching Mystic and Angus over the days they had visited the park. He immediately noticed that Angus' dark countenance had changed. Now his face fairly glowed. A bright smile that seemed to stretch from ear to ear accented his face. He did not even look like the same man.

"Well, uh, water you say, from Jesus?" stammered the Ranger. "Jesus was down by the stream?" he asked as he looked down in that particular direction, with a very puzzled look on his face. The Ranger was not being sarcastic, just confused.

Angus suddenly realized how confusing his comments must be to the poor Ranger. He burst out laughing, leaned over and put both hands on his knees until he gained his composure. When he looked up, the Ranger was looking back at him with an expression of sincere anticipation. Angus knew he wanted to know more.

"I am sorry," said Angus. "Let me simply put it this way. I have been depressed for months since the death of my wife. This moose has been telling me about the power Jesus has to help people. I took him at his word, asked Jesus to help and He did. I am suddenly so encouraged and feel so free that when I saw you I could not help but tell you about this Jesus."

Tears welled up in the Ranger's eyes. He stammered, "My wife and I are at our wits end. Last week our youngest daughter ran away from home after a terrible argument with her mother. What can Jesus do about that?" he implored.

MYSTIC HAS WORD OF KNOWLEDGE

Mystic said, "Is her name Darlene, and does she have a friend name Ginny?"

Startled, the Ranger said, "Yes, how did you know? I didn't tell you her name and I certainly did not tell you her friend's name. Ginny is a year older and is in the university an hour away. She could be with her!"

Mystic said, "I know from the Lord that Darlene is with Ginny, and I believe she wants to come home but does not know if you will take her back."

The Ranger said, "I know her parents. I'll get Ginny's phone number and find out how to get there. I want my daughter back. Wow! Jesus is real."

With that he ran over to his truck to get his cell phone. He hopped in, started his truck as he called his wife to find Ginny's phone number. As he drove out of the lot, he rolled down his window and waved.

Mystic thought to himself, "How amazing is the life of God. It flows so easily out of lives that He has freshly touched." Then he prayed, "Lord Jesus, thank You so much for saving Angus McAlpine. I really love him and know that You must love him much more. Thank You for touching his life."

With that, the two of them hopped into Angus' car and headed back to Magellan's house.

C H A P T E R   7

FORGIVENESS

Angus, the once depressed, borderline morose writer, emerged from the waters of baptism unusually exuberant. Jesus changed his life and he wanted the world to know it. His conversion was no "just go to church and keep quiet" affair. He was on fire. At a whole new level he wanted to know any and everything Mystic had to say about the Son of God and the spiritual life. He chomped at the bit to spend time with him and record whatever he had to say.

The abrupt change in R. Angus McAlpine startled Mystic. He was hard to startle. Mystic's spiritual life strained most folk's understanding capacity. First of all, by way of reminder, he was a talking moose, *genus–Alces Americana Southernanas*. Secondly, he functioned as a high order supernatural believer in Christ Jesus. Thirdly, his legendary encounters with God were highly suspect to folks who didn't understand him or believe there could be a 'him' quite like Mystic Moose. He authenticated a prototypical Holy Spirit filled lover of God who lived in fulltime pursuit to know Him more. He also exuded extraordinary kindness.

MYSTIC AND ANGUS ENGAGE AGAIN

"Mystic, everything seems so new today; colors are so bright and the air seems so clean. It's like I breathed deeply for the first time in my life. I had no idea what I was missing!" Angus collected Mystic once again at Magellan's house.

"Last night I dreamed about Marilyn. I saw her in heaven. She was walking away from me in a field of flowers of brilliant colors I had never seen before. She walked with someone I didn't recognize. Could've been an angel, I don't know much about that. I have missed her so much. I called out to her to stop. She turned, looked at me, and my heart flip-flopped inside my chest. She said, 'I can't come to you, but one day you will come to me. Soon you will understand, but for now, trust God. I must go.'

"I woke up almost weeping, Mystic, not from sadness but from great joy. I even laughed out loud on my bed. I miss her with all my heart, but I know I'll see her again. I remember the night before she died she had a peace I didn't understand. I do now. Her folks raised her Southern Baptist. She said she had a salvation experience in summer camp when she was twelve years old. I didn't want to talk about it, but she did, particularly that last night. That kind of conversation made me uncomfortable. I think she knew the end was near but I couldn't even...." Angus' voice trailed off, tears easing out of his eyes.

"...T'was much too painful . . . for me to consider." Angus regained his composure. "Now I know that Jesus really saved her at that summer camp. I should have talked to her about it, but I was never willing to talk about her faith. Ridiculous really, not to talk about something this important with someone I loved so much. Not now, I'm so ready to talk about Jesus that I'm about to pop. I'm full of whatever it was He did to me yesterday–that new life you've been talking about."

MYSTIC REJOICES

"Angus, Jesus is wonderful. I am thrilled you met Him yesterday. He is *amazingly* wonderful. Actually, that's one of His names, '*Wonderful*, Counselor, Mighty God, Prince of Peace.'[42] I want the whole world to know Him."

THE GLORY ZONE

At that, Mystic and Angus spontaneously began thanking God over and again. For a few moments they were lost in profuse praise so excessive that it seemed to charge the very atmosphere. Mystic called it "the glory zone." He lived in a continual state of praise and thanksgiving, but this was something even greater, much richer and packed with energy. Angus was ready to live in that state with him.

"God lives in praise, Angus. King David penned a song describing Him as the God that dwells in the praises of Israel.[43] He knew it was true. I am afraid that many of God's people have lost the art of entering into His presence with praise. God is willing to trade down so we can trade up. He gives us a garment of praise for a spirit of depression."

ANGUS WONDERS, MYSTIC SENSES

"Awesome, Mystic. Keep it comin'. I'm all ears. I'm learning such new things from you all the time."

Angus grew silent.

Mystic sensed that he wanted to ask him something personal but hesitated to do it. He had an amazing capacity to sense what others felt even before they expressed it.

"What is it Angus? Is there something you want to ask me?"

---

42   Isaiah 9:6
43   Psalm 22:3

"On my way over this morning, I thought about you a lot. You've spoken of your difficult church experiences as a child. You described the encounter you had with the angel in the Animal Scouts. Such conflicting experiences. How did you get here from there?" Angus probed.

MYSTIC CONTINUES HIS STORY

"It's complicated," Mystic began. "As you recall, the angel visited my mother when she was pregnant with me. God healed her from the cancer. That triggered the revival at the First Full Blown Holy Ghost Gospel Fellowship where Mom and Dad went to church before I was born. They told me years later that season was like heaven on earth. So many people were deeply touched by the power of the Spirit. Lives were changed. Marriages were restored. God affected a whole generation of young teenagers. As a result of her healing, I was born a healthy, bouncing baby moose."

THE GOOD, THE BAD, THE UGLY

"'*The Good, the Bad, and the Ugly*', the name of an old Clint Eastwood western, best describes those days. Obviously, 'the Good' involved the healings and restorations. 'The Bad' and 'the Ugly' soon followed. The church, and Mom and Dad in particular, came under an intense persecution. Criticism flowed like an overwhelming flood. Some area churches were particularly hostile. Even pastors spread rumors that Mom was a witch and that she was practicing the occult. They said that the odd occurrences in their church were of the devil. That's the '*kiss of death*' level accusation in those circles. It deeply wounded my parents. Their initial encounter with the angel and what the Lord did in those days made God so real to them. It caused them to fall in love with Jesus Christ like never before. The persecution caught 'em completely off guard. They naively assumed everybody would be as excited as they were that God was doing such wonderful things.

"My parents weren't equipped to handle the intense criticism that arose from the outpouring of the Holy Spirit of those days. They had no grid to understand the wonder of it, nor the fallout following fast on its heels. They struggled with bitterness. Their attitudes affected me as a boy. I was too young at first to understand what happened, but as I grew up I realized the toll it took on their lives. The church they loved became cold, boring, and dry out of a reaction to all the criticism about them. I lost interest in religion, maybe not altogether in God, but at least in organized religion."

RANKLING DULLEDGE RHINOCEROS

"One particular pastor led the charge against the outpouring–Rankling Dulledge Rhinoceros, Sr. Remember him, Angus? He was the pastor of the local God Used to Do Miracles But Not Now denominational church. Later he became known in our community and more widely through local media circles as '*The Bible Know It All*'. Rhinos have a reputation in West Africa for stomping out campfires wherever they find them, a most unusual characteristic. Some say that's only legend. True or not, Rank Rhinoceros did all he could to stomp out the Holy Spirit fire that started in The First Full Blown Holy Ghost Gospel Fellowship years ago. Rhinos have poor eyesight. It may be from the two horns that sit so prominently on their nose, just in front of their eyes. True to genus, Rankling couldn't *see* that the wondrous events at Mom's church originated in heaven. He aired his criticisms of the church and Mom in particular on his radio show. At one point, Mom and Dad and their pastor met with him to discuss his charges, long after he denounced them. By his own admission the testimonies of the changed lives and the quality of the people whose lives Jesus affected amazed him. He never backed off his criticism though. I guess it would have been too humbling for him to reverse fields over the airwaves."

WHY?

"Why would he do that, Mystic?" asked Angus.

"Good question, I'm not sure why. Only God knows a man's motives. He became quite popular, attacking what *he said* was non-scriptural practices in the church. He built part of his ministry on doing that. His public correction of other believers without talking to them is hypocritical. If you're 'The Bible Know It All,' you should practice the clear teachings of the Bible, one would assume. The Bible identifies the process for correcting one another; go to them first and confront them with their clear unscriptural practices or sins. If you haven't been honestly heard or heeded, take a witness of the practices with you and confront them again.[44] Only then should you consider going public with your charges. He rarely obeyed that biblical practice.

"His intentions could have been sincere, but you can be sincerely wrong. He acted like he was protecting other Christians from heresy. Throughout history sincere people have done great damage to the works of God. Jesus warned His disciples that 'the time is coming that whoever kills you will think that he is doing God a favor.'[45] Angus, that's how deceived people can be.

"His relentless attack confused many who had life-changing experiences. My parents became very confused. Dad left the church and became bitter for a time by the pain it caused my Mom. The young people suffered the most. Many who had significant life changing encounters with the Lord were sidetracked, some even shipwrecked by the attack and confusion that came."

JESUS' WARNINGS

"Jesus warned His followers that persecution was inevitable. 'A servant is not greater than his master. If they persecuted Me, they will

44   see Matthew 18:15-17
45   John 16:2 The Message Bible

persecute you,' He said.[46] A wise old British preacher friend of mine used to tell me, 'Mystic, persecution is God's income tax; the more income, the more tax. Little income, little tax. No income, no tax.' It comes with the territory.

"Jesus was especially concerned with the young. He warned, 'It is impossible that no offenses should come, but woe to him through whom they do come! It would be better for him if a millstone were hung around his neck, and he were thrown into the sea, than that he should offend one of these little ones.'[47] Angus, you must never accuse or persecute others, even if you disagree with them. The Lord doesn't like that. Persecutors will have much to answer for at the final judgment. Every disagreement or confrontation of evil should be done with dignity. Everyone should be treated in an honorable way."

THE FEAR FACTOR

"People will often attack or defend things based on how fearful they are. Some react that way to spiritual occurrences that are outside of their experience or church tradition. Because of some of the warnings in the scripture others are deathly afraid of deception. Some have more faith in the devil's ability to deceive than in the Holy Spirit's ability to lead into truth.

"In some conflicts it's hard to tell who is right and who is wrong. Oftentimes, both parties are right and wrong."

"How do you determine who is right?" asked Angus.

"Relative to the supernatural realm, one must answer these three questions," Mystic said. "Is Jesus honored and glorified by what is happening? Are people helped? Does it create in you a hunger for more of God? If it doesn't, then something is off-track. If it does all of those things, you can be assured God is in it."

---

46   John 15:20 RSV
47   Luke 17:1-2

WHO IS ATTACKING?

"Identify the aggressor, Angus. The Apostle Paul said that the man inspired by the sinful, selfish nature persecutes those whose actions are inspired by the Holy Spirit.[48] The one who persistently attacks is motivated by his base nature. Some have confused criticism with discernment, Angus, but any jackass can kick down a barn. It takes wisdom and grace from God to build something of note. Who's building and who's tearing down? That's the issue."

WHAT ABOUT YOUR PARENTS?

"Mystic, did your parents ever get back on track? I am saddened that after such wonderful things happened to them they became so discouraged."

"Oh, yes. They got back on track Angus. It took a number of years and another crisis. More about that later. First, let me catch you up to speed on how Jesus captured my heart. Back when Skunk Larry and I arranged the church sanctuary flood—you remember that story, don't you?"

"Of course. Who could forget that sad, soggy, situation."

MYSTIC REMINISCES

"Well, after the time of the great flood (man I'll never forget the whipping I got for that), while sitting in church, sometimes my mind drifted back to my encounter with the angel in the woods during the Animal Scouts campout. I had mixed emotions about it. Who wouldn't be terrified by such an unusual experience? I was, but I could not escape a sense of excitement and energy when I remembered all that the angel said and did. At least it wasn't boring.

"I remembered the words spoken by the angel with the large blue 'B' on his sweater: 'Fear not young Theodore, for the Lord has sent

---

48   Galatians 4:20

me to tell you His grand purpose for your life. He has called you to preach the everlasting gospel of the grace of God to many people in many places. As you proclaim the wonders of Christ Jesus, signs and wonders shall follow and healings will be multiplied. You shall influence a great number of young people as they find new life in the Lord, Himself.'

"I couldn't reconcile the awesomeness of that experience with the kind of religious life I saw week after week. When I asked Mom and Dad about the way church was, they gave me some vague answers but often they recounted stories of the revival just before I was born. The supernatural stories intrigued me and my heart burned when I heard them. I didn't really know why."

MYSTIC'S CHILDHOOD DREAM

"One Sunday shortly after Skunk Larry and I unleashed the flood waters and sabotaged the meeting, I found myself back in church bemoaning my fate. I gave 'jazzing up the assembling of the righteous' my best shot and it didn't take. I surrendered. Afterwards I would much rather be out running with my buddies, playing ball and getting into mischief. As I sat there through the sermon and thought about these things, I drifted off to sleep and dreamed. Or at least I think I was dreaming. What I saw seemed real.

"In the dream I was some years older and found myself in a spacious open style building. It looked like a warehouse with tall ceilings, lots of brickwork, a lot of windows, and wooden beams. Some kind of corporate gathering was in session. I knew instinctively that it was a church meeting, but a kind I never experienced before. People there were exuberantly talking about the Lord. The music and singing was much more powerful and exhilarating than any kind I ever experienced. The worship had an authentic feel to it. Hope abounded in the atmosphere. It was as though God Himself was there. Some people were happy and rejoicing with great abandon. Others were on the floor on their faces, worshiping and praying. The room felt charged with electricity or some kind of vibrant energy. I felt more alive than ever.

"Children played a vital role. I saw some young children get up and speak with authority to random members of the congregation. They proclaimed the most remarkable insights. They spoke words of incredible encouragement. Some of them were no more than seven or eight years old. Teenagers arose and spoke powerfully. Some said but one sentence while others spoke for five to ten minutes. In each case, extraordinary power and grace were released to all who listened. They identified sicknesses that folks had and prayed for them. Some were weeping and were healed.

"The time of worship was so powerful it reminded me of both the fear and electricity I experienced when the angel appeared to me in the woods years earlier. A man I didn't know walked over to me and said, 'This waits for you in the future. Pay attention.' At that point in the dream I felt a sharp stabbing pain in my ribcage on the left side that woke me up. Lamar, Skunk Larry's brother, who sat next to me in the pew when I fell asleep poked me in the ribs.

"'Wake up you idiot,' Lamar said. 'You're drooling all down the front of your shirt. You look like a derelict!'

"So, Angus, that's how I awoke from the dream that imparted to me a new vision for church, with Lamar Skunk poking me in the ribs and mocking me!"

High School and the Hit Record

"By the time I was a freshman, my whole life focused on Chubby Bascom and the Slippery Slopes," Mystic said.

"Who?"

"Chubby Bascom and the Slippery Slopes, the band a bunch of us started at Walt Woodchecker Sr. High School, home of the Fighting Toads. With such a lame mascot, there was no way we were gonna field a championship sports team of any ilk. We tried, but when your opponents mock you with 'ribbet, ribbet, got any warts?' you don't even take yourself seriously. We gave up sports and gravitated toward guitars, drums, loud amps, and the girls. Sad to say, but we started the band for most of the wrong reasons."

THE HIT SONG

"The band did amazingly well. Turned out we had some talent. We played a form of Southern blues/rock. I wrote a song named *Sweetness Belinda* that skyrocketed in our area. The song hit # 4 on the Nations Top Forty Chart. One of the local radio stations picked it up. Quick as a snail on steroids we were really rolling. Ralph Sprocket signed us to a record deal after we won a local battle of the bands. Hermione and the Warthogs came in second. That's just what Lamar's band deserved. Go figure, Hermione and the Warthogs. What a dumb name. All of us had to buy bigger hats to fit our swelling heads. Every weekend and all summer long we played all over the Southeast."

THE MENAGERIE INCREASES

As I got to know Mystic Moose, I discovered he had a knack for collecting an odd but interesting assortment of highly entertaining friends. To say that some of them were unusual is the ultimate understatement. And the stories he told–if I had not come to know him so well, I would have doubted much, sometimes even most, of what he said about his eclectic menagerie of associates he claimed as compatriots. He stretched my capacity to believe him more than a hippopotamus would stretch a skinny guy's spandex riding tights. Bulges of unbelief abounded!

THE BULLDOG

Once again Mystic launched. "About that time I met a dog named Spartacus Archibald Johnson, the bulldog with a heart of gold. He became one of my closest associates during one particularly intense and fruitful season of my ministry. You realize, Angus, that I spent over sixty years in ministry. He became an integral part of Motherlode Church, a congregation I pastored for four years.

"Spartacus spent his earlier career in law enforcement, attained black belt status in Karate, and was skilled in personal protection. He told me he felt the presence of God more when helping people than at any other time. He was very protective of those he loved or those for whom he felt responsible. He had a reputation for being bullheaded and determined. I found him to be unusually kind, even sensitive, but he hid that part of himself pretty well. His bark was much worse than his bite until someone was in danger. Then his bite became ferocious. Search a thousand years and you couldn't find a more loyal canine than Spartacus. I admired him. He was the kind of guy I enjoyed running with."

MEETING THE BULLDOG

"After Skunk Larry and I started Chubby Bascom and The Slippery Slopes, our sudden popularity wrote checks our maturity couldn't cash."

"Huh? Mystic, sometimes your colloquialisms lose me in a hurry. And who was Chubby Bascom? You've never mentioned him."

"Oh, sorry Angus. Who was Chubby Bascom? He was a janitor in our elementary school."

"What did he have to do with your band?"

"Nothing. We just liked his name," Mystic answered. "Had a good ring to it. Better by far than Hermione and the Warthogs."

THE ODD COLLOQUIALISM

"I mean, that after my song shot up the charts, the band's popularity grew like an over fertilized field of kudzu. Our music got us into situations we weren't mature enough to handle, hence our popularity wrote checks our maturity couldn't cash. The band consisted of Skunk Larry and I on guitar and vocals, Livingstone on bass, Alley 'By jiminy' Gator on accordion and violin, and Fat Bobby Porker on drums. The personality mix got us into some pretty hairy situations. We traveled almost every weekend during the school year. Every summer break from school we traveled for almost three months straight. We lived on four hours sleep many nights, traveled between gigs, and generally lived on the edge.

"One night in Smyrna, Georgia, we just finished our last set at the Blue Bonnet Club owned by a guy named Boss Spearman, a retired former cowboy from west Texas. A fight broke out. Remember now Angus that all of this happened before I got back to serving the Lord. Fat Bobby did not 'suffer fools gladly' and had some attitudinal adjustments of his own he needed to make. Some pigs just won't back down from an altercation. Fat Bobby fit that description to a 'T'. He got into a shouting match with a redneck *gentleman* who had spent a good part of the night trying to disrupt our gig. Bobby was not the smartest pig in the litter. He didn't realize that some rednecks run in packs. When I turned around, I discovered Fat Bobby in a full body contact melee with four of them down by the bandstand, and it was not going well for him at all. As large as he was, we lost sight of ole Bobby amongst a flurry of flying fists, kicking boots, and high level screaming and cussing.

"Larry and I ran down to help him, but before we got there a big burly bulldog jumped in the middle of 'em and knocked down three of the four of 'em. He grabbed up Fat Bobby like he was light as a feather, threw him out of harms way, and went back at the guys who were beating on him.

"The bulldog shouted over his shoulder at Fat Bobby, 'You better run fat boy before these guys make bacon out of you!' And to the two of us, 'That goes for you as well moose and skunk.'

"Fat Bobby landed on his back and rolled up under our feet. After he stood up, the three of us watched the bulldog do his thing. He was 'black belt Karate Tai Kwon Do mixed martial arts' poetry in motion.

"That bulldog spun around in a circle as fast as greased lightning while *executing* this Karate kicking maneuver. 'Executing' was the operable description. I've never seen anything like it, before or since. Inside a New York minute, all four of Fat Bobby's adversaries were writhing and groaning on the floor in various states of execution. That bulldog tore 'em up. At one point he had chomped down on the ringleader's ankle and wouldn't let him go. You know those bulldogs. When they get a hold of you, you can't shake 'em *a'loose*. He tore 'em up so bad that I started to feel a little sorry for 'em. I tried to get the manic bulldog to let go of the one he was chewing on. It wasn't until Fat Bobby ran up and appealed to him that he eased up his bite. That 'puppy' was not playing.

"At the time none of us knew who he was. I wondered why he jumped into the fight to begin with. After the dust settled and those guys limped away in abject defeat, Bobby and I introduced ourselves."

NO BULLYING ZONE

"His piercing blue eyes sparkled brightly as he spoke, 'Hello. I'm Spartacus Johnson. I can't abide bullying in any form! I saw your friend's dilemma and determined to even the score.'

"That answered my question. 'Thanks for the help. I thought we were going to lose Fat Bobby for a second there.'

"'Nope. That wasn't going to happen. Not on my watch. I like your music too much. I've been following you since I first heard you guys at the battle of the bands. I've been watching them boys all night long. I could tell they were going to cause trouble before the night was over, probably before they knew they were. It's sort of a sixth sense I have,' Spartacus said.

"'I've been around law enforcement and worked security details for years. I'm always on the alert even when I'm out in public. Can't turn it off. I stay alert to potential trouble everywhere I go.'

"Angus, we got to be good friends with Spartacus Johnson. Whenever one of our gigs was within driving distance from his house, he would join us on the road. He became like a non-musical member of the band. Later that summer our manager Ralph Sprocket decided we could hire a road manager/security man and allocated enough funds for it. We hired Spartacus. He kept us alive more than once. He worked for us for the better part of a year, but then the Lord got a hold of us and the band went through some major changes. I lost track of the bulldog. I heard that he went to work for an up and coming TV ministry."

RECONNECTING WITH THE BULLDOG

"A number of years later, Spartacus showed up at Motherlode Church. He experienced a profound seven+ year spiritual odyssey that left him disoriented and deeply disappointed. He became head of security in a ministry that took off like a meteor led by a thirty-year-old innovative preacher named John Steward. He really was a creative genius. He accomplished more in ten years than any five great preachers do in a lifetime.

"The ministry proved to be more blessed than they had the capacity to handle. Their television show became wildly popular and their ability to mobilize financial support was extraordinary. However, along with the success came temptation and compromise fueled by too much work and eventual burnout. If Satan can't stop what you are doing, then he tempts you to initiate more than you can handle. Many great leaders have opened more fronts than they can support.

"The pressure rose and John Steward fell. Throughout the history of the ministry they waged an unwise running battle with the news media. Some delighted in finding fault with Christian ministries, particularly ones that raised large sums of money. Steward's ministry made itself extremely vulnerable to attack. One problem created another. His marriage fell apart. Creditors hounded him to pay for his many ministry expansions. Ultimately, the Federal government took him to court and charged him with various illegal financial dealings. He was tried, found guilty, and sentenced to prison. Some concluded the court's findings were unjust. Nevertheless, Steward went to prison, and after a long, painful season, the ministry succumbed to defeat.

"Spartacus lived for the success of that ministry. He served with all his heart. True to form, he was tenacious, stubborn, and fiercely loyal. After a dismal and demoralizing finale, he called it quits and had to find his way out of what had become a terrible spiritual wilderness.

"The news media had a field day reporting and re-reporting images of the destruction. John Steward, Spartacus, and many others suffered beyond their ability to endure.

"Years later, after serving his sentence, Steward quietly exited prison. In an effort to take responsibility for what he had done and to explain his side of the episode, he wrote a book that became a *New York Times* bestseller entitled, *I Messed Up Bad . . . Real Bad!* It contained inaccurate and hurtful information about Spartacus. By then the bulldog had become a major part of my church and served on our board of directors. He resigned from the board after deciding to retaliate. He knew enough about John that had never been reported that would re-damage his reputation. It would probably be widely reported. Spartacus didn't want the bad publicity to hurt our church."

THE BOOK HITS THE STANDS . . . AND SPARTACUS

"After the book hit the stands, Spartacus read it. The Sunday morning following, I watched him walk into my church looking like a man sentenced to death. The book reignited painful memories of all that happened years earlier and hit him like a sledgehammer.

"During worship, Spartacus sat near me on the front row close to the worship team. He saw one of our worship leaders about to fall, so he got up to be sure she didn't hurt herself. Before he could get close to her, he fell on the floor under the power of the Holy Spirit. I knew that was the work of God. He prided himself in always being in control."

THE INCREDIBLE ROOM, THE BOOK OF HIS LIFE

"Angus, a most amazing thing happened. Spartacus Johnson found himself in a supernatural place standing before a large impressive door. He pushed the door open and entered the room. A lavishly appointed library full of hundreds of thousands of impressive wood-bound books stretched out before him. The floor, the walls, the ceilings, the bookshelves, and the book bindings were constructed of the finest polished wood. An unusual energy impregnated the atmosphere. Spartacus struggled to communicate to me the wonder of the great library hall. He determined he would never leave that place.

"The chief bookkeeper, an impressive authoritative man, stood before him. He guarded the books yet had no authority to add to or take from them. Spartacus' eyes locked down on one particular book with his name etched in gold on its cover. It rested upon an ornate gold stand accented with detailed filigree.

"People of every ethnic background filled the vast library. It reminded him of New York's Grand Central Station except it was much quieter. Many were dressed in clothes from different cultures and ages, like unrecognizable costumes. The room contained many books just like his on stands for each person who stood beside his own book slowly turning the pages. Some spoke quietly with their own bookkeepers as each person searched through his volume. He could tell that many of them seemed nervous. Spartacus began to feel nervous too. He knew he was about to read heaven's book of his life. He was deathly afraid of what he would find. He wondered if it recorded all his sins. His bookkeeper stood ready to help him in whatever way he could."

THE POWER OF FORGIVENESS

"With great trepidation Spartacus Archibald Johnson opened his book before his bookkeeper. He began reading the literal story of his life in the order it had occurred. He read of his birth, where he attended school, of the birth of his sister, the dog he loved as a child, the death of his grandfather. He cringed as he approached certain too familiar events as his transcribed life's story unfolded before him. A wave of fear and shame began to engulf his heart. When he arrived at places in the book where he expected to read about his sinful acts, they were blank. It looked like something had been there, but nothing was written there now. Those pages were completely blank, not just absent of words, but transparent, even translucent. Looking at those particular pages was like looking down through eternity. His sins were nowhere to be found. First shocked, then relieved, Spartacus wondered, 'Where are they?' He asked the bookkeeper, 'What was written there? Is there nothing written there?'

"'No one knows,' his bookkeeper answered. 'No one at all!'

"Spartacus marveled at the absence in heaven of any record of the sinful things he did on earth. He suddenly realized how thoroughly Jesus forgave him. A huge burden he carried for many years fell from his shoulders like a heavy weight.

"He knew, 'Nothing anyone on earth could say or write about me shall ever condemn me again. No longer can I be intimidated or shamed by anything I have ever done. It's all gone.'"

Angus Comes Unglued

"Mystic, does that mean all my sins are gone?"

"Yes, Angus, they are all completely gone for one reason and one alone: Jesus took them. He took your sins, your punishment. You are free forever!"

Angus began to weep. It took him a long time to regain his composure. Mystic waited a long time as Angus sobbed deeply.

One Free Bulldog

"For the first time in his entire life, Spartacus felt completely healed of his past. The depth of his forgiveness saturated his whole being. He felt like he had been washed, not just outwardly but throughout his entire being. 'Nothing written in any earthly book can ever have an evil hold on me again,' the liberated bulldog exclaimed."

The Power of those Heavenly Books

"Spartacus realized that all the books in that library were amazing, unique, and extraordinarily supernatural. Of his personal volume he said, 'That book was alive.' That was as close as he could come to accurately describing it."

Forgiving Others

"As his new revelation began taking hold of his mind, one thing momentarily dismayed him. Some of the people who hurt him deeply had books there too. Their sins were not recorded either. He knew he couldn't hold anything against them if he wanted to enjoy the freedom his heavenly book ensured. He let it all go; he let go of all his resentment of everyone who had ever sinned against him."

Time to Go

"Then the bookkeeper said, 'Spartacus, it is time for you to leave.' He didn't want to leave and emphatically refused to budge. 'No. I'm not going back. I'm stayin' right here forever,' he said. He determined no one could remove him from that wonderful place. He hunkered down on the floor and with all his strength wrapped his arms and legs around a nearby table leg.

"The bookkeeper said one more time, 'Spartacus, it's time for you to go.' He wasn't about to leave. The bookkeeper turned to two other angels and said, 'He is a strong one. You'll have to remove him.' They effortlessly picked him up by the back of his coat collar and his belt, carried him through the door, gently sitting him down outside the Library. As they carried him through the door of the Library, he saw its name for the first time. In bold red liquid letters the sign read: The Hall of Forgiveness.

"Upon regaining consciousness, he lay on the floor of the church exactly where he fell twenty minutes earlier. He became painfully aware of his surroundings and of his own physical body. Like never before he became aware of himself and his internal organs. He could literally feel the toxins that were in his liver. He was back on terra firma and utterly dismayed to be so.

"Spartacus never recovered from the glory of his encounter in the heavenly realm. It put a deep yearning in his heart to return to that place. He said, 'If that's not heaven, well, it's good enough for me!'"

CHAPTER 8

BACK
ON TRACK,
THE HARD WAY

"Mom's cancer returned the fall after my senior year at Walt Woodchecker Sr. High. I knew she hadn't been feeling well, but I had no idea she was that sick. That October our band had a gig at a venue in Alexandria, Va. Dad called. He said he hated to tell me over the phone, but Mom's cancer had returned. It didn't look good. I needed to come home as soon as I could. Alexandria was the last stop on a two-week tour.

"Chubby Bascom and the Slippery Slopes had grown much more popular. Our manager, Ralph Sprocket, was in the prelim stages of negotiating a two-night gig at the Boston Garden as the opening act for 'The Morris Minor Band.' It would have been the next step into the major markets, maybe a national tour."

"I thought the Lord healed your mom from cancer just before you were born," said Angus.

"He did. Back then Skunk Larry's mom and her crowd prayed for her and Jesus touched her with a healing heat. The tumor disappeared, verified by her physician. She was cancer free for ten years. She carried me full term and, voila, 'Here I am.' I don't understand how one gets healed of cancer and it returns, Angus, but the reality was that she contracted a different kind of cancer in a very aggressive form. The oncologist estimated that she had but 4-6 weeks to live."

"What did you do?"

"Cried... then got mad... cussed a while, then blamed God," said Mystic. "What else was an eighteen-year-old kid going to do that wasn't walking with God. I was living for myself. I wanted to be rich and famous, and counted on my music to get me there. If I had known at eighteen years old what I know now at seventy, I would have reacted much differently. It's never His fault. It's dishonest to live on our terms and then blame God when our way doesn't work."

"But, Mystic, what did you do?"

POWER OF REMEMBERING

"Angus, I knew I needed to connect with the Lord in a fundamental way. I wasn't quite sure how to do it. The reality of my childhood angelic visitation in the woods kept coming back to me. That provided me with some hope. Skunk Larry had a similar encounter the same night. He told me that he saw what happened to me from the edge of a clearing near my campsite. We scarcely spoke of it, just once since we were young kids. It frightened both of us. We didn't really know how to process the experience. We both knew it would estrange us from our friends. 'Hi, I'm a moose who talks to *letter sweater clad sword wielding* angels in the woods. Want to be friends?' That wasn't going to work. We didn't understand it. How would they?

"The older we got, the less I thought about, or tried to *not* think about it. At times I wished it never happened. It almost haunted me. When the band became so successful we were sitting on top of the world, until Mom's cancer returned. There was not one soul in all this world I loved more. She decided to go through chemotherapy. I watched her hair fall out. She lost so much weight. Sometimes she became so tired she could but speak above a whisper. When I was with her I acted cheerful. I tried to encourage her, but when I was alone I agonized. I cried a lot. Watching her was so painful. I couldn't bear it. There was nothing I wouldn't do to help her.

"I decided I must do something radical, but I needed a partner. Who better than Skunk Larry, my very best friend, my comrade in arms since childhood. He saw the angel. He heard his words. The angel spoke to him too. He would listen to me."

Teddy Moose (Mystic) and Skunk Larry Plot and Plan

"I phoned Skunk Larry. 'Lawrence Skunk!' (I called him his given name whenever I had something serious to say.) 'If something doesn't happen for Mom, she's not going to make it.'"

"I know Teddy. Mom and I went by to see her last night. Mom prayed for her but is really worried at the same time. She doesn't look very good." Skunk Larry said. "What can we do?"

"I don't know. I think… (I hesitated a second) …maybe we should go back to the exact place in the woods and try to find that angel. Sounds crazy I know, but that's all I got right now. I'll come over and we'll get our heads together."

At Larry's House in His Bedroom

"I rushed right over to Larry's house. When I arrived, he sat in his room looking at an old wrinkled up piece of cardboard with some stuff written on it."

"Larry, remember the words the angel spoke over us in the woods? He said that we could see people healed, but I don't know how to make it happen. I don't even know where to start. I thought you and I may ought to go back to the place where he appeared to us."

"And do what?" Larry responded.

"I don't know… camp out a couple days, build a fire, wait, hope . . . pray maybe. I don't much know how to pray. I'm not much good at it. What do you remember about what the angel said when he appeared to you?"

"I remember most of it. I scribbled it down on the back of this cardboard cereal box just after I got back to my campsite that very morning. I have read and re-read it many times since it happened so many years ago. Here it is!"

Larry handed Teddy *that* very piece of cardboard. Before Teddy came into his room, he pulled it out of his sock drawer to read it again.

Teddy looked at it and handed it back to Larry. "Tell me what you remember."

"I didn't get everything exactly as he said it but this is what I did get…" Larry began.

"At the first the angel called you by your whole name, 'Theodore Conquest Moose.' I didn't know your middle name until then Teddy, but he knew it. Then he told you to stand up in front of him. Teddy, you were so afraid. I'm not sure when it happened exactly, but at one point I was sure I could hear your boney knees knocking together. I couldn't help but laugh." Larry snickered again then right in Teddy's face.

"Come on, Larry, what did he say!"

"He told you not to be afraid. He said you were supposed to be a preacher and that you would do it in a bunch of places. He said that many young people would be affected and that something he called signs, wonders, and healings would happen."

"Man! I remember some of that. I was terrified. Then what?"

"You dove under some bushes or whatever was there. One leg was sticking out. He reached down and picked you up by your ankle. He sort of flipped you around in mid-air and you floated down to the ground. I never saw anything like it before. It's almost like gravity was partially suspended."

"I'll never forget him picking me up. Then he picked up his sword, didn't he?" Teddy remembered.

"Yes. I saw it glisten in the early morning light. Then he tapped you with it a couple of times, said something else, and seemed to disappear in the campfire's smoke. Weird, huh?"

"Yes, weird, but I'll never forget that part either."

"Teddy, next thing I knew, he was standing in front of me. I got scared too. I'm not even going to tell you what I did. He said that we were called to work together, and that many needed to hear our message or their lives will be lost forever. He said many who are sick do not need to be, and that Jesus would use us to help them get healed. He also told me that we would meet others in the future who would help us, train us, and inspire us. He warned that some people would misunderstand us and get mad about what we were doing. He promised me that we would never fail if we always trusted the Lord. Then he smiled and disappeared."

A Plan Unfolds

"Larry, let's go back to the woods, back to the place where it all happened. Maybe the angel will come back and talk to us, or maybe we'll find out how to get Mom healed. I'm desperate. I don't know what else to do, or where to go. Will you go with me?"

"Teddy, we've been friends our whole lives, even when Lamar tried to sabotage us. At great peril you stopped Dr. Pepper and that hideous nurse Wilma Waddle from poking my fingers day after day when I was sick. You helped me become captain of the basketball team. You showed me the best time I ever had in church when we flooded the sanctuary. We've ridden the musical heights together with Chubby Bascom and the Slippery Slopes. Now your Mom has cancer. I don't know what to do either. We have to do something. Let's give it a shot. Count me in. To the woods we shall go."

OFF TO THE WOODS

They gathered together sleeping bags, a tent, food, water, matches, firewood, extra baloney (had to have baloney), marshmallows, and a myriad of other quasi-necessities. The two adventurers struck out at once for the woods to the very place Colonel Dumpford first dropped them off in pursuit of their Animal Scouts Courage and Bravery merit badges. They returned to the scene of their mutual encounter with the heavenly being who proclaimed God's supernatural call on their lives. They knew not what to expect. They could scarcely imagine what may happen. They only hoped, perhaps even believed that they could reconnect to their lost destinies and find God's power to help Teddy's Mom get healed.

Just before they left Teddy's house, he popped into his Mom's room to kiss her goodbye. He told her what they were doing as best as he could explain. Tears filled her eyes, then Teddy thought he saw a spark of hope in her slight smile too.

MOM'S INSTRUCTIONS

"While you two are there," she said, "ask for God's help in the name of Jesus Christ. He promised that if two people agree asking for anything in His name, He would do it. Ask Him to help me."

It had been over ten years since Teddy or Skunk Larry were in those woods. At first they couldn't identify the exact location of

Teddy's original campsite. They thought they knew about where it was, but the forest had grown so much over the years. Then Teddy spotted the rickety remains of the lean-to he built on his original trip to the woods.

"Here we go Larry," Teddy said. "This must be what's left of my lean-to. Not much to behold, some pieces of blue tarp blowing in the breeze and that one slat attached to that old oak."

They set up camp. Larry fussed with the telescoping tent poles for over an hour before he figured out how the contraption went together. By then it was late afternoon. The crickets chirped in high gear. The robins were hopping around on the ground nearby looking for worms.

"I like the way those birds cock their heads sideways as they look for food," Teddy said of the robins. "They are a good sign for us Larry. They are known as the harbingers of a new season. I hope they are signaling a new season of life for Mom."

The sun crept down below the not-too-distant evergreens. Daylight turned to dusk and the air began to chill just a little. Larry built a fire, coat hangered their first marshmallows of the expedition, and settled in for night numero uno. Teddy plopped down a few round slices of kosher baloney on a clean flat rock that was heating up.

"Nothing quite like a few pieces of fried baloney to inaugurate the camping trip, Larry."

"I like fried baloney almost as much as I like you, Teddy," Larry joked. "It soothes a skunk's soul like little else can, except maybe a roasted hot dog on a toasted bun with extra hot mustard and some Vidalia sweet onions, and an ice-cold Cheerwine."

From the corner of his eye, Teddy thought he spotted a distinct stream of drool slip out of Skunk Larry's mouth as he spoke of the hot dogs. They both dug into the baloney. Two pieces led to four more apiece. By the time they engulfed them all, Larry had some grease on his shirt that arrived there via the corners of his mouth and then his pointed chin.

"That boy do love him some baloney," thought Teddy. "Glad *I'm* not baloney. Better still, glad I'm not a roasted hot dog. I would not be long for this world, not around him!"

The two outdoorsmen settled in to the campsite as the stars came out from their hiding. Such a blanket of heaven's light they hadn't seen in years. They were over ten miles from the city lights that could obscure the clear view. Neither decided to sleep inside the tent. Spreading out their sleeping bags near the fire and lathering up with some Deep Woods Off to befuddle the mosquitoes, the moose and his close friend eased into the blanket of night. As they lay on their backs under the night's canopy, they began to watch a short-lived meteor shower. Shooting stars raced across the heavens in a marvelous display.

THE BOYS BEGIN TO PRAY

Teddy began praying for the first time in years, "Lord, heal my Mom. I don't know how to do it but I'm asking You to do it, for her and for me."

Larry followed. "Yes. Mom Moose told us to ask in Jesus' name. She said if we agreed and asked in Your name, You would do it."

A few quiet moments followed. Teddy began again, "Lord Jesus, please heal my Mom. She's too young to die. I love her too much."

Tears dripped down his cheeks and into his ears. Teddy was not confident that his praying was going to work. He sat up on an elbow and looked over at Skunk Larry with such great sorrow, his eyes sagging under the stress and strain of his pain.

"I'm going to sleep Larry. See you in the morning."

"Goodnight buddy," Larry said. "This is going to work. I don't know how it'll work, but I believe God is listening to us." Larry rolled over in his sleeping bag and tried to snooze too. Sleep didn't come easy for either of them that night.

TEDDY AWAKENS

About five in the morning, Teddy began to stir. He hadn't slept very well. Sitting up in his sleeping bag, his eyes began to focus a little. It was still too dark to see anything. Something had startled him awake, more like a feeling than something that happened. He felt that nervous sensation he had as a young Animal Scout, like when he looked into the star laden heavens and wondered about never ending space. It was the way he felt that night before the angel appeared to him.

"Psst…Larry…are you awake?"

"Most of the night, Teddy, most of the night," Larry said.

"Do you feel something strange?" Teddy asked.

"Yes… for about a half an hour. I've been too scared to open my eyes. What is it? Why do we both feel like this?"

"This is the way I felt just before the angel appeared to me as a child," Teddy said. "I think maybe something important is about to happen."

THE OPEN VISION

By now both boys sat up together, peering into the darkness. The unusual feeling grew in intensity. It became a kind of presence. Both of them looked up in the darkness as they heard an unusual whirling sound. A small colorful circle appeared suspended in midair, not far away but very close, just a few yards ahead of them. Out of the flat one dimensional blackness of night, in an explosion of sight and sound, a full-fledged technicolor 3-D vision opened before the eyes of both Teddy and Skunk Larry. Larry's jaw dropped open and his eyes bugged out like one of those odd South American geckos on the

World Archeological T.V. show. Teddy sat perfectly still, mesmerized by the sights, sounds, and smells.

Before them unfolded an unusual scene. In the foreground a large group of murmuring Roman soldiers milled about anxiously in the ancient room. Their rough appearance matched their harsh uncouth manner. The dusty sweat-stained tunics they wore complemented the crudeness of their speech. Several of them erupted in laughter only to be silent just as abruptly. The room they occupied spanned about forty feet by fifty. The fifteen foot ceiling had open barred windows whose shutters were propped open. Irregular hewn limestone formed the floors and walls. It smelled of mildew and body odor.

One of the members of the Roman garrison stood guard at the rough-cut oak door located in the back of the room. It was the only way in or out. The guard answered a pounding on the door. He swung it wide open as it groaned aloud on its iron hinges. A cadre of raucous legionnaires hurried into the room pushing and cursing one lone man. Teddy could see he had already been severely beaten. The centurion gathered the soldiers together and announced, "The crowd demanded Pilate release Barabbas the murderer. He sent us this man in his place. Prepare him for crucifixion." The soldiers in the room responded like they anticipated his arrival. They cheered and jeered as the single prisoner fell into the room having been cruelly shoved forward. Tension mounted by leaps and bounds.

"All hail the king of the Jews," one of them mocked. Jesus of Nazareth had arrived. Everyone's eyes riveted upon Him.

Teddy whirled around, smacked Larry in the arm, and whispered, "Are you seeing this Larry? That's Jesus!" Larry saw exactly what Teddy saw, shocked and so consumed by the mesmerizing scene that he could not summon even a slight response.

THE VISION CONTINUES

The soldiers laughed and mocked Jesus over and again. They acted as though making sport of Him was their pleasurable privilege. They tied His wrists together with a leather cord securing Him to an iron ring embedded in a limestone pillar in the center of the room. He was no common criminal. Even in this humiliated condition, the dignity of His being commanded everyone's attention. All the while, members of the garrison cursed Him and spat in His face. One of them blindsided Him with a forceful open hand slap to His head, knocking Him down. His attacker snarled, "Prophesy to us, King of the Jews. Who struck You?" Cascades of derisive laughter rained down upon Him, the vanquished carpenter of Nazareth.

After being struck to His knees, the leather cords binding Him to the rusty iron ring were His lone support. One of the most powerful soldiers pushed his way through the garrison carrying an odd looking whip. Called a cat of nine tails, the implement of punishment had a wood handle attached to nine leather straps embedded with jagged iron shards. "Stand back," the legionnaire boomed. "It's time to determine what this king is made of."

Over and again the muscular Roman lashed Jesus across His back. Each time He was struck, Jesus leapt in agony, both feet leaving the ground. He reacted like some wild animal being punished by its angry master. The leather cords wrapped around His ribcage as each stroke grabbed and dug into His flesh, leaving deep bleeding furrows across His back and shoulders. With each stripe, blood spurted from His torso. His back and sides became one open gaping wound pouring blood.

Teddy Moose jumped up from his sleeping bag and shouted to the soldiers in the scene before him, "Leave Him alone. What has He done to you? Leave Him alone."

Teddy stood still, looking intently at the graphic scene before him. As though Jesus heard Teddy's plea, He turned His head toward the young moose. Their eyes met. Through His battered bleeding face, Jesus smiled at him but for a moment. His eyes were bruised and almost swollen shut. Blood ran down His face. Blood ran everywhere. Jesus' smile completely broke Teddy's heart. He fell to the ground near the ashes of the cold campfire, weeping until he could weep no more.

When Teddy looked up, the soldiers had placed on Jesus a crown platted of three-inch long thorns so sharp they penetrated deeply into His head. One shouted, "Every king deserves a crown." For a time they clothed Him in a purple robe. When they tore it off Him, all His wounds poured blood again. Jesus had been beaten beyond recognition.

The door swung open again. One of Pontius Pilate's chief officers ordered, "Bring the prisoner with me. Pilate said it's His time. Take Him to the place of the skull and crucify Him there with the other two." One legionnaire pulled a dagger from his scabbard, cutting Him free from the iron ring. They led Him away through the throng of mocking, spitting soldiers, out the door in the back of the room. The Son of God pushed forward towards His destiny.

NATURE GROWS SILENT

In a state of shock, Teddy Moose and Skunk Larry stood without moving a muscle. The wind stopped blowing. The leaves didn't rustle. The crickets were quiet. Even the nearby babbling brook was stilled by the graphic display of the suffering Savior. Nature itself became silent in respect for the Son of God. The two sobbing friends made the only sounds heard in those parts of the woods that night.

HE APPEARS

Teddy and Larry regained their composure and stood looking at one another in silence and awe. Both knew that this vision changed their lives forever. Heavy fog crept into their campsite "on little cat feet" just as Carl Sandburg once wrote. It was so dense they could see no more than ten feet beyond their small area. Out of the fog strode Christ Jesus Himself. He stood before the two young friends.

He wore another brilliant crown, this one not of thorns. His eyes radiated an intense fire. His hair was white as fine wool. Teddy saw His hands. They didn't have scars but holes that were completely healed. Light poured from them. The two boys fell at His feet. Jesus reached out and lifted each boy up, one with each nail scarred hand. Then He spoke:

"I came to My own and My own did not receive Me. I suffered for your sin and your healing, like the Prophet Isaiah foretold, 'But He was wounded for our transgressions, He was bruised for our iniquities; the chastisement of our peace was upon Him, and by His stripes we are healed.'[49] I died on the cross and rose from the dead so that you may live. Look what I have done for you, and your Mom.

"Many refused Me. Will you refuse Me too? Will you walk away from Me or will you walk with Me?" Jesus' penetrating gaze fixed upon Teddy and Skunk Larry for a short moment that seemed like an eternity to them. Without another word, He turned and walked back into the fog. He was gone as quickly as He appeared.

TEDDY'S PROMISE

"Larry, as Jesus spoke, my heart burned inside me. Like an overwhelming flood the promise I made ten years ago came back to me as though it had been written on my burning heart. How could I have forgotten? As a young moose I said, *'Lord, if You want me to do the stuff that angel told me, then I will do so with all of my heart. Let me know what You want me to do and when You want me to do it and I will give it my best shot.'* He has certainly let me know this night. I mean to do just what I promised."

---

49   Isaiah 53:5

Larry looked at me and said with identical determination and conviction, "Teddy, I'm in!"

"Pack up Larry. Let's head for home. It's time to see Mom restored. I know Jesus will heal her. How can this cancer stand before Him?"

BIOGRAPHY
ROBIN MCMILLAN

Born and raised in the Reformed Presbyterian tradition of his forefathers, Robin has been a believer since his salvation encounter with Christ Jesus during the Jesus Movement of the late 1960's. He has planted two churches and pastored four over the past 25 years. Currently he is the Senior Pastor of Queen City Church in downtown Charlotte, N.C.

For 14 years he functioned in several capacities with MorningStar Ministries, three years as Director of MorningStar Fellowship of Ministries and Churches, and 11 years as Senior Pastor of the church in the Charlotte, NC area. In addition to overseeing the church he wrote for the MorningStar Journal, taught in the school of ministry, and spoke in their many conferences.

His passion is to awaken the church to the power of the Holy Spirit to touch the world, to equip believers to discover how they can access the realm of the heavens, enjoy the presence and power of God, and be empowered to live supernatural lives. Outpourings of the Holy Spirit, outbreaks of joy, and demonstrations of power and healing often accompany his ministry.

Robin and Donna, his wife of 36 years, have four children and four grandchildren.

TO CONTACT THE AUTHOR:

Email: Robinmc1111@gmail.com

Blog: robinmcmillan.me

TO ORDER ADDITIONAL BOOKS:

Additional books may be purchased at www.robinmcmillan.me.

WHO MEN SAID THAT I AM

Christ Jesus Himself once asked His disciples 'Who do men say that I am?'. There is no more significant question than this one. An accurate, heart felt, faith-filled, revelation based answer insures eternal life.

"As a child I received instruction both in the Bible and in the Talmud. I am a Jew, but I am enthralled by the luminous figure of the Nazarene. No one can read the Gospels without feeling the actual presence of Jesus".

Albert Einstein

"I know men and I tell you that Jesus Christ is no mere man. Between Him and every other person in the world there is no possible term of comparison. Alexander, Caesar, Charlemagne, and I have founded empires. But on what did we rest the creation of our genius?

Upon force. Jesus Christ founded His empire upon love; and at this hour millions of men would die for Him."

Napoleon Bonaparte

"Despite our efforts to keep him out, God intrudes. The life of Jesus is bracketed by two impossibilities: 'a virgin's womb and an empty tomb'. Jesus entered our world through a door marked, 'No Entrance' and left through a door marked 'No Exit'."

Peter Larson

"I am trying here to prevent anyone saying the really foolish thing that people often say about Him: 'I'm ready to accept Jesus as a great moral teacher, but I don't accept His claim to be God.' That is the one thing we must not say. A man who said the sort of things Jesus said would not be a great moral teacher. He would either be a lunatic — on a level with the man who says he is a poached egg — or else he would be the Devil of Hell. You must make your choice. Either this man was, and is, the Son of God: or else a madman or something worse. You can shut Him up for a fool, you can spit at Him and kill Him as a demon; or you can fall at His feet and call Him Lord and God. But let us not come with any patronizing nonsense about His being a great human teacher. He has not left that open to us. He did not intend to."

C. S. Lewis

"Jesus Christ is to me the outstanding personality of all time, all history, both as Son of God and as Son of Man. Everything he ever said or did has value for us today and that is something you can say of no other man, dead or alive. There is no easy middle ground to stroll upon. You either accept Jesus or reject him."

Sholem Asch

"No one else holds or has held the place in the heart of the world which Jesus holds. Other gods have been as devoutly worshipped; no other man has been so devoutly loved."

John Knox

"Buddha never claimed to be God. Moses never claimed to be Jehovah. Mohammed never claimed to be Allah. Yet Jesus Christ claimed to be the true and living God. Buddha simply said, 'I am a teacher in search of the truth.' Jesus said, 'I am the Truth.' Confucius said, 'I never claimed to be holy.' Jesus said, 'Who convicts me of sin?' Mohammed said, 'Unless God throws his cloak of mercy over me, I have no hope.' Jesus said, 'Unless you believe in me, you will die in your sins.'"

Unknown

"Jewish authors would never have invented either that style or that morality; and the Gospel has marks of truth so great, so striking, so utterly inimitable, that the invention of it would be more astonishing than the hero. Shall we suppose that the evangelical history is a mere fiction? Indeed it bears no marks of fiction; on the contrary, the history of Socrates, which no one presumes to doubt, is not so well attested to as that of Jesus Christ."

Jean Jacques Rousseau

"I have always been impressed by the fact that God is happy - and that this ineffable and continuous joy lived in the soul of Christ. Joy is for me a transport, a state of drunkenness in the 'maddest' sense of the term."

Olivier Messiaen

"I am an historian, I am not a believer, but I must confess as a historian that this penniless preacher from Nazareth is irrevocably the very center of history. Jesus Christ is easily the most dominant figure in all history."

H.G. Wells

"Jesus promised His disciples three things: that they would be entirely fearless, absurdly happy, and that they would get into trouble."

W. Russell Maltby

"Jesus is the God whom we can approach without pride and before whom we can humble ourselves without despair."

Blaise Pascal

"God may thunder His commands from Mount Sinai and men may fear, yet remain at heart exactly as they were before. But let a man once see his God down in the arena as a Man--suffering, tempted, sweating, and agonized, finally dying a criminal's death--and he is a hard man indeed who is untouched".

J.B. Phillips

"For thirty five years of my life I was, in the proper acceptation of the word, nihilist, a man who believed in nothing. Five years ago my faith came to me. I believed in the doctrine of Jesus Christ and my whole life underwent a sudden transformation. Life and death ceased to be evil. Instead of despair, I tasted joy and happiness that death could not take away."

Leo Tolstoy

"After six years given to the impartial investigation of Christianity as to its truth or falsity, I have come to the deliberate conclusion that Jesus Christ was the Messiah of the Jews, the Savior of the world and my own personal Redeemer." (A one-time atheist, Lew Wallace was a military general and literary genius, who along with Robert Ingersoll agreed together they would write a book that would forever destroy the myth of Christianity. Mr. Wallace studied for two years in the leading libraries of Europe and America for information to destroy Christianity. While writing the second chapter of his book, he suddenly found himself on his knees, crying out, 'My Lord and my God.' The evidence was overwhelmingly conclusive.)

General Lew Wallace

"I say unequivocally that the evidence for the resurrection of Jesus Christ is so overwhelming that it compels acceptance by proof which leaves absolutely no room for doubt." (**Sir Lionel Luckhoo** is considered by Guinness book of world records to be one of the worlds most successful trial lawyers. He won a world record 245 murder acquittals in a row. As such Sir Lionel is well versed in the appreciation and understanding of the conclusiveness of evidence.)

Sir Lionel Luckhoo

Simon Peter said of Him: "You are the Christ, the Son of the living God".

We need to know Him. What do you say about Him?

How to get started:

Even the best among us has sinned. The very smallest one of our sins is evidence we owe God a debt we can't repay, and the wages sin pays is death. But God has made the forgiveness of that debt possible by paying for it Himself. Jesus died for us *as* that payment, but His death does us no good until we accept by faith that He alone could and did pay for it. That kind of faith in Jesus obtains our personal forgiveness. That kind of faith is expressed by believing with all your heart in Jesus, is obtained by confessing that Jesus is Lord, and walked out by turning from sin.

1. **Everyone needs salvation because we have all sinned.**
    Romans 3:10-12, and 23

    As the Scriptures say, "No one is righteous—not even one. No one is truly wise; no one is seeking God. All have turned away; all have become useless. No one does good, not a single one." ... For everyone has sinned; we all fall short of God's glorious standard. (NLT)

2. **The price (or consequence) of sin is death.**
    Romans 6:23

    For the wages of sin is death, but the free gift of God is eternal life through Christ Jesus our Lord. (NLT)

3. **Jesus Christ died for our sins. He paid the price for our death.**
    Romans 5:8

    But God showed his great love for us by sending Christ to die for us while we were still sinners. (NLT)

4. **We receive salvation and eternal life through faith in Jesus Christ.**
    Romans 10:9-10, and 13

    If you confess with your mouth that Jesus is Lord and believe in your heart that God raised him from the dead, you will be saved. For it is by believing in your heart that you are made right with God, and it is by confessing with your mouth that you are saved ...For "Everyone who calls on the name of the Lord will be saved." (NLT)